Grade 4

Practice Book O

Macmillan
McGraw-Hill

The *McGraw·Hill* Companies

 **Macmillan
McGraw-Hill**

Published by Macmillan/McGraw-Hill, of McGraw-Hill Education, a division of The McGraw-Hill Companies, Inc.,
Two Penn Plaza, New York, New York 10121.

Printed in the United States of America

10 066 09 08

Contents

Unit 2 • Take a Stand

Unit 3 • Making a Difference

Unit 4 • Viewpoints

Unit 5 • Relationships

© Macmillan/McGraw-Hill

Unit 6 • Discovery

| allergies | assignments | suspicious | accuse |
| consideration | consume | evidence | |

**Write a complete sentence to answer each question below.
In your answer, use the vocabulary word in bold type.**

1. Why would a detective be **suspicious** if someone got caught telling a lie?

_____

2. How does a detective make sure that **evidence** is not destroyed?

_____

3. What does a detective give careful **consideration** to?

_____

4. Will a detective **accuse** someone when all the clues are in?

_____

5. Did the suspects come to the table only to **consume** a meal?

_____

6. If Tanya has **allergies,** can she avoid sneezing at the crime scene?

_____

7. Do detectives get **assignments** every day?

_____

Now use one of the words above in a sentence of your own.

8. _____

A story usually begins by introducing a character and the **problem** he or she has. The steps the character takes to solve the problem are the **events** of a story. A story ends with the **solution** to the problem. The problem, events, and solution make up the **plot** of a story.

Read the passage and each question. Underline the answer in the passage and then write the answer.

A box came in the mail for Denisha, but it had no return address. When Denisha opened the box, she found a blue jacket and matching pants. She tried on the pants and jacket. They fit perfectly, and blue was Denisha's favorite color. She wanted to thank the sender. She asked her mother and sister if they had mailed the package, but they both said no. Denisha looked again at the outside of the box, and then she smiled. "I figured it out! The stamp says that the box was mailed from Detroit. Grandma lives there. She must have sent it."

1. Who is the main character? _____

2. What is the problem? _____

_____

_____

3. What is the first thing Denisha does to solve her problem? _____

_____

4. How does Denisha solve her problem? _____

_____

5. What might happen next? _____

_____

© Macmillan/McGraw-Hill

At Home: Have the student select two or three favorite books and tell you the main character, problem, and solution in each.

As you read *The Mystery of the Missing Lunch,* fill in the Problem and Solution Chart.

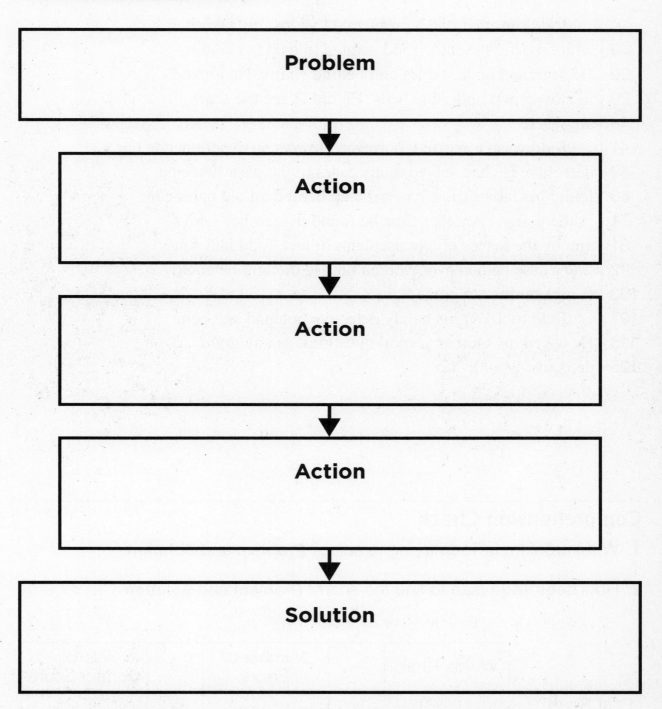

Problem

↓

Action

↓

Action

↓

Action

↓

Solution

How does the information you wrote in the Problem and Solution Chart help you to analyze *The Mystery of the Missing Lunch*?

At Home: Have the student use the chart to retell the story.

The Mystery of the Missing Lunch
Grade 4/Unit 1   **3**

Name _____

As I read, I will pay attention to end punctuation in each sentence.

	Todd's mother had a problem. "I've lost my favorite
9	white scarf," she said. Todd wanted to help her find it.
20	He searched under tables and behind chairs. He looked
29	in closets and under the beds. He didn't see the scarf
40	anywhere.
41	Todd wasn't worried, however. He was an experienced
49	detective. He had solved many cases in the past. Once he
60	found his father's lost baseball cap behind an old paint can
71	in the garage. Another time he found his mother's keys
81	among the leaves of a houseplant. In fact Todd had solved
92	every case he had ever worked on. He thought he could
103	complete this assignment, too.
107	Todd took out his handy detective notepad and pen.
116	He asked his mother several questions, as any good
125	detective would. 127

Comprehension Check

1. What problem is Todd trying to solve? **Problem and Solution**

2. How does Todd plan to find the scarf? **Problem and Solution**

	Words Read	–	Number of Errors	=	Words Correct Score
First Read		–		=	
Second Read		–		=	

© Macmillan/McGraw-Hill

At Home: Help the student read the passage, paying attention to the goal at the top of the page.

A **chart** is a good way to organize information.

Erik asked third-, fourth-, and fifth-graders in his school what kind of mysteries they have solved. The chart below shows what he learned.

Use the information in the chart to answer the questions.

Kind of Mystery	Number of Students	Percent of Students
Found a missing object	47	58%
Found out who did something	21	27%
Found out what happened	12	15%

1. What kind of mystery did most students solve? _____

_____

2. How many students found out what happened? _____

3. What percent of students found out who did it? _____

4. What percent of students found a missing object? _____

5. Were there more students who found out what happened or more

students who found a missing item? _____

_____

6. If some students said they had never solved a mystery, how would you

change the chart? _____

_____

At Home: Look in the student's nonfiction books or in newspapers and magazines for charts. Help the student read the information.

Look at this dictionary entry for an unfamiliar word. Use the definition and sample sentence to help answer the questions that follow.

> **purloin** *verb* **1.** to steal; to take something secretly and without permission. *He planned to* purloin *the diamonds.*

1. What does *purloin* mean, in your own words?

_____

2. Use *purloin* in another sentence.

_____

3. How would you find the meaning of the word *abscond*?

_____

4. Write the meaning of *abscond* below.

_____

At Home: Find unfamiliar words. Together, determine the meanings of the words and create sample sentences for each word.

Name _____

Each vowel has a long and a short sound. The **short vowel sounds** are as follows:

a as in *flat*   **e** as in *shelf*   **i** as in *mill*   **o** as in *blot*   **u** as in *sum*

When a vowel is in the middle of two consonants, it usually has a short sound.

Read the sentences below. Circle each word that has a short vowel between two consonants.

1. The police found the cash behind the shelf.

2. One thief ran to the dock.

3. One thief had a plot to steal the bell.

4. The thieves hid behind a big tree.

5. They lay flat on the grass.

Circle the words with short vowel sounds. Then use three of them in sentences.

plate   left   bleat   cove   load   mill   past   neat   leave   crunch   plum

6. _____

_____

7. _____

_____

8. _____

_____

At Home: Go through a favorite story or magazine article with the student and challenge him or her to find as many short-vowel words as possible.

The Mystery of the Missing Lunch
Grade 4/Unit 1

7

climate	silken	lumbering	swallows
lurk	shimmer	eerie	

Substitute a vocabulary word for the underlined word or words in each sentence.

1. The rattlesnake's rattle makes a <u>scary</u> sound, warning us to keep out of

its way. _____

2. Alligators often <u>lie in wait</u> in the reeds until small animals come near.

_____

3. A bear's <u>heavy, awkward</u> step warns small creatures in its path.

_____

4. The surface of frozen ponds <u>glow brightly</u> in the winter sunlight.

_____

5. Cacti are plants adapted to <u>dry weather for most of the year</u>.

_____

6. A snake <u>gulps</u> its prey without chewing. _____

7. A spider's web is made of <u>soft, smooth</u> strands. _____

Choose three vocabulary words and use them in one sentence.

_____

_____

_____

Name _____

> The **main idea** of a selection tells you what it is all about. The supporting **details** in the selection help you to understand the main idea. The main idea is often, but not always, stated in the first sentence.

Read the passage and answer the questions that follow.

Many newborn rattlesnakes do not survive their first year of life. A baby rattlesnake is only about 10 inches long. Although they have short fangs and a poisonous bite, they are often eaten by birds and animals. The adult rattlesnakes do not raise their young. The young snakes are entirely on their own. Many die of hunger. In the winter they die if they do not find a warm place where they can hibernate.

1. What is the main idea of this passage?

_____

2. What supporting details tell you how young rattlesnakes are in danger? List two details on the lines below.

_____

_____

_____

3. What supporting detail tells you how baby rattlesnakes can survive in the winter?

_____

4. What supporting detail tells you how baby rattlesnakes can attempt to defend themselves?

_____

© Macmillan/McGraw-Hill

At Home: Together, look for short paragraphs in books and newspapers and ask the student to identify the main idea and supporting details.

As you read *A Walk in the Desert*, fill in the Main Idea Chart.

Main Ideas	Details

How does the information you wrote in the Main Idea Chart help you
to summarize *A Walk in the Desert*?

At Home: Have the student use the chart to retell the story.

Name _____

As I read, I will pay attention to tempo.

	The Sahara is the world's largest desert. It is nearly
10	the size of the United States. The Sahara extends over
20	10 countries in northern Africa. Like all deserts, it gets
29	fewer than 10 inches (24 cm) of rain a year.
37	In parts of the Sahara, you can see nothing but sand for
49	miles. A sand dune forms when wind carries sand over a
60	large rock. The sand drops, and gradually a hill of sand
71	grows.
72	However, about 80 percent of the world's deserts are
80	not sandy. This is true within the Sahara as well. Deserts
91	begin as rock. The rock is worn away and broken apart by
103	wind, rainstorms, and changing temperatures. Over time,
110	the rock is broken into smaller and smaller pieces. The
120	rock breaks down first into boulders, then into stones, and
130	finally into sand. In some places, the Sahara is made up of
142	huge rocks and gravel. 146

Comprehension Check

1. What makes the Sahara a desert? **Main Idea and Details**

2. State the details of how a desert is formed. **Main Idea and Details**

	Words Read	–	Number of Errors	=	Words Correct Score
First Read		–		=	
Second Read		–		=	

© Macmillan/McGraw-Hill

At Home: Help the student read the passage, paying attention to the goal at the top of the page.

A Walk in the Desert
Grade 4/Unit 1

11

Name _____

Assonance is the repetition of the same or similar vowel sounds in two or more words. For example:
   We pl(ay)ed in the r(ai)n tod(ay).
A **metaphor** compares two different objects or ideas and states that one is the other. For example:
   A hawk is a feathered airplane circling in the desert.

Read the poem and then answer the questions.

Cactus

Tough spiny plant.

Water hiding inside.

A secret, shaded oasis for me.

1. What two things are being compared in this metaphor?

   _____

2. How is a cactus like an oasis?

   _____

3. What words in the poem are an example of assonance?

   _____

4. On the lines below, write a metaphor about one of the following.
   desert tortoise   wood rat   rattlesnake   roadrunner   lizard

   _____

   _____

At Home: Have the student write a metaphor about a common household object.

Sometimes **surrounding words** can provide the context you need to figure out the meaning of an unfamiliar word.

Read the following sentences. Circle the answer with the words that best fits in the blank.

1. A **border** _____ often separates one country from another.

   a. of green flowers   **b.** such as a river

2. **Venomous** snakes, _____, kill prey with their poisonous bite.

   a. including rattlesnakes   **b.** in the zoo

3. In the west, the open **range** of _____ gradually became fenced in.

   a. empty plains   **b.** deep lakes

4. Many desert animals hide from **predators** _____.

   a. like cows   **b.** such as foxes

5. At high **elevations** _____ there are fewer trees and plants.

   a. under the ocean   **b.** near the top of mountains

6. **Fledglings,** _____ hatch from eggs in the spring.

   a. such as baby wrens   **b.** such as full-grown hawks

7. **Nocturnal** animals, _____, look for food between dusk and dawn.

   a. like bats and owls   **b.** like whales and dolphins

8. Western farmers plant **orchards** full of _____.

   a. orange and lemon trees   **b.** chickens

At Home: Think of a word that is unfamiliar to the student. Then give him or her the word in a sentence with words around it that help explain its meaning.

A Walk in the Desert
Grade 4/Unit 1   13

The long *a* sound can be spelled the following ways:
ay tod<u>ay</u>, str<u>ay</u>   **ai** r<u>ai</u>l, dr<u>ai</u>n   **a_e** sl<u>a</u>t<u>e</u>, gr<u>a</u>z<u>e</u>
ei n<u>ei</u>gh, sl<u>ei</u>gh   **ea** br<u>ea</u>k, gr<u>ea</u>t

Read the following sentences. Write the words in the sentences that have a long *a* sound on the lines below.

1. The baby wood rats played outside today.

_____

2. Does it take long to make a crate for a rattlesnake?

_____

3. Rain in the desert can cause a great flood.

_____

4. Desert sunsets paint the sky bright colors.

_____

5. Did you see the snake that just slithered across the trail?

_____

6. Don't break away from the trail when walking in the desert.

_____

7. We heard the stray horses neigh as they grazed on desert bushes.

_____

8. We hiked in the desert until my legs ached and I felt faint.

_____

© Macmillan/McGraw-Hill

At Home: Have the student write three sentences that each use at least two words with the long *a* sound.

Name _____

Read the vocabulary words. Use the clues to complete the puzzle.

roamed   completed   journey   natural   wildlife

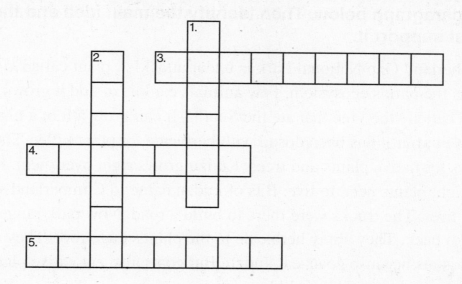

Across

3. finished
4. trip
5. untamed animals

Down

1. wandered
2. not artificial

Write a sentence using two of the words.

6. _____

_____

The **main idea** of a selection tells you what it is about.
The supporting **details** in the selection help you understand
the main idea.

**Read the paragraph below. Then identify the main idea and three
details that support it.**

Cumberland Gap National Park is under attack! A plant called *kudzu*
threatens the park's ecosystem. Few animals eat kudzu and it grows so fast
it's been called "the vine that ate the South." It can grow a foot a night! It
grows even after it has been dosed with herbicide, or plant killer. That's
bad news for native plants and trees. Kudzu grows right over them. It takes
the sunlight plants need to live. Bits of kudzu came to Cumberland stuck
to truck tires. The trucks were there to build a road. Now park rangers
cut kudzu back. They apply herbicide to the plant's huge root. They could
bring in goats because goats eat kudzu. But goats also eat native plants.
Solving the kudzu problem will be tricky.

1. Main idea:

_____

_____

2. Supporting detail:

_____

3. Supporting detail:

_____

4. Supporting detail:

_____

© Macmillan/McGraw-Hill

At Home: Together, choose a topic that someone might
write about. Talk about what the main idea might be and
what details could be used to support it.

Name _____

As you read *Animals Come Home to Our National Parks,*
fill in the Main Idea Chart.

Main Ideas	Details

How does the information you wrote in the Main Idea Chart help you
to summarize *Animals Come Home to Our National Parks*?

 At Home: Have the student use the chart to retell the story.

Animals Come Home to Our
National Parks • Grade 4/Unit 1

17

© Macmillan/McGraw-Hill

As I read, I will pay attention to the pronunciation of vocabulary words and other hard words.

	Acadia National Park has dark green mountains. When
8	you look down from these mountains you see the icy
18	Atlantic Ocean. You see ocean waves crashing against
26	rocky shores. These 48,000 acres (194 sq km) of **natural**
34	beauty have a long history. It is a history full of stories
46	about people who loved this land of mountain and sea.
56	These people worked to make sure that everyone could
65	enjoy it.
67	Acadia National Park is spread out over a group of
77	islands off the coast of Maine. Most of the park is on
89	Mount Desert Island. The park has beautiful freshwater
97	lakes and ponds. There are trails for hiking in the
107	mountains or walking by the shore.
113	As you read, you will learn about the history of
123	this park. 125

Comprehension Check

1. What is the main idea of the first paragraph? **Main Idea and Details**

2. What details would you use to describe the natural beauty of the park? **Main Idea and Details**

	Words Read	−	Number of Errors	=	Words Correct Score
First Read		−		=	
Second Read		−		=	

© Macmillan/McGraw-Hill

At Home: Help the student read the passage, paying attention to the goal at the top of the page.

Name _____

A dictionary entry lists more than just a word's meanings. It also includes its pronunciation, part of speech, and examples of how to use the word.

Read the dictionary entry below. Then answer the questions that follow.

entry word   example of word in a sentence

first meaning of word — **lively 1.** full of energy. The *lively* puppies romped around the room.

second meaning of word — **2.** bright. The walls of Emma's room were painted a *lively* pink.

pronunciation
syllable division — **live·ly** līv′ lē *adjective,* **livelier, liveliest.**
other forms of the word

part of speech

1. What is the entry word? _____

2. How many syllables does this word have? _____

3. To pronounce the word *lively,* is the vowel in the first syllable long

   or short? _____

4. What part of speech is *lively?* _____

5. Which definition best describes a fourth-grade class at recess?

   _____

6. What other forms of *lively* are listed in the entry? _____

   _____

At Home: Have the student write two sentences using both meanings of the word *lively.*

Name _____

> A **compound word** is made up of two words. If you know the meaning of both smaller words, you can usually figure out the meaning of the compound word.

Put a mark in the underlined word to show the two separate words. Then answer the question.

1. Becky wanted to find an old Cherokee <u>arrowhead</u> on her family's camping trip.

   What does it mean? _____

2. They built a <u>campfire</u> on high ground to make supper.

   What does it mean? _____

3. When the park ranger stopped by, Becky's dad gave him a <u>handshake</u>.

   What does it mean?

   _____

4. The park they were in had birds, deer, and other <u>wildlife</u>.

   What does it mean? _____

5. The woods were full of <u>evergreen</u> trees, such as pine and fir.

   What does it mean? _____

At Home: Help the student identify compound words that describe objects you find around or near the house, such as *mailbox*.

> The letters **ea, ee,** and **ie** often stand for the long **e** sound, as in **mean, meet,** and **thief.**

Use the following words to complete the riddles.

> leave   beef   please   bee   piece   peeling   cheese

1. What do you call a cow on the ground?

   ground _____

2. What do you call a fly with one wing and two noses?

   I don't know, but when you find out, _____ let me know.

3. Why did the boy eat his homework?

   His teacher told him it was a _____ of cake.

4. Where do you _____ your dog while you shop?

   at a barking lot

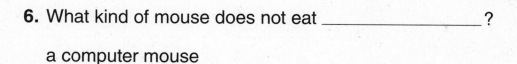

5. Why did the banana go to the doctor?

   He wasn't _____ well.

6. What kind of mouse does not eat _____ ?

   a computer mouse

**Circle any other words you find in the riddles with the letters ee,
ea, and ie.**

At Home: Together, look for words with the long *e* sound in
books or magazines.

Name _____

endless	universe	protested	realistic
sensible	astronaut	paralyzed	

Replace the underlined words with one of the words from the vocabulary list.

1. He was an excited <u>space traveler</u> zooming toward Mars. _____

2. I <u>complained</u> about traveling alone. _____

3. A trip in space may seem <u>without a finish</u>. _____

4. The film about space travel was <u>the way things are</u>. _____

5. His plan for launching a rocket was not <u>well thought-out</u>.

_____

6. Scientists are studying <u>everything in space.</u> _____

7. The astronaut seemed <u>unable to move</u> when he climbed outside the

spaceship. _____

Use three of the vocabulary words in sentences of your own.

8. _____

_____

9. _____

_____

10. _____

_____

Name _____

Understanding the **characters** and the **setting** can help you understand what happens in a story.

Read the passage. Then answer the questions that follow.

When she was little, Andrea lived near the Kennedy Space Center. Her mother always took her there to watch the rockets launch. As Andrea grew up, she realized that she wanted to do more than just watch rocket launches. More than anything, she wanted to be an astronaut, but she wasn't sure that she could be one.

Her mother told her, "If you want something, the important thing is that you try your best." Andrea ate well and exercised. She studied hard in all her subjects. After college she learned to fly jet planes.

Andrea's dream came true. She became an astronaut and took many trips into space.

1. Who are the characters in this story?

_____

2. What is the setting when Andrea is a little girl?

_____

3. How did Andrea's mother help her achieve her goal?

_____

4. In most plots, a character changes. How did Andrea change in the story?

_____

_____

_____

At Home: Ask the student to describe a character from a favorite story.

Name _____

As you read *The Astronaut and the Onion,* fill in the Character Web.

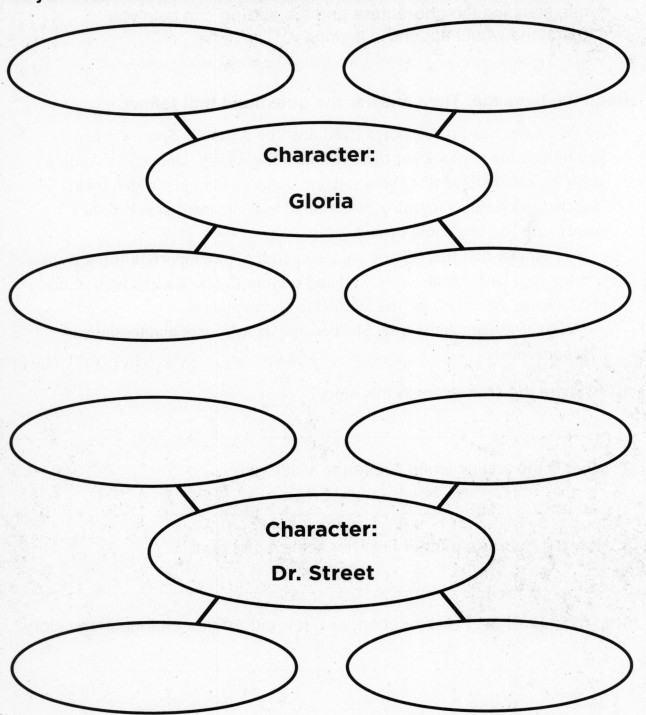

How does the information you wrote in the Character Web help you analyze and make inferences about *The Astronaut and the Onion*?

At Home: Have the student use the chart to retell the story.

© Macmillan/McGraw-Hill

Name _____

As I read, I will pay attention to pauses, stops, intonation, and the characters' words.

	Rahul was staring anxiously out the spaceship window.
8	"Mom, how long 'til we get there again?" he asked.
18	His sister Shona laughed. "Rahul, didn't you just ask her
28	ten minutes ago? And she said two hours?"
36	From her seat at the control panels, **Astronaut** Amla
45	Gupta smiled. "Now kids," she said, "there's no point in
55	arguing about it. We'll get there when we get there. Why
66	don't you play with the other kids? I thought I saw Carlos
78	and Keisha and Fatima playing space tag on the landing."
88	The Guptas were on their way to Space Station 88
97	for the summer with ten other families. The station had
107	been abandoned for 50 years.
111	Now the space station was needed for research. So the
121	families would spend the summer fixing it up. In the fall,
132	a caretaker would live there. 137

Comprehension Check

1. What are the families going to do at Space Station 88? **Character**

2. What kind of people are Rahul and Shona? **Character**

	Words Read	–	Number of Errors	=	Words Correct Score
First Read		–		=	
Second Read		–		=	

At Home: Help the student read the passage, paying attention to the goal at the top of the page.

A **diagram** is a drawing that presents information. Some information is easier to understand by looking at a diagram.

Lengths of American Rivers

St. Lawrence—760 miles

Brazos—840 miles

Columbia—1,150 miles

Colorado—1,450 miles

Mississippi—2,350 miles

Use the diagram to answer the questions.

1. What is the diagram about? _____

2. What rivers are included? _____

   _____

3. Which river is longest? Which is shortest? _____

   _____

4. What can you use this diagram to do? _____

   _____

5. Where in the diagram would you put a river that is 1,320 miles long?

   _____

At Home: Help the student make a diagram of a room in your home.

When you are reading and come to a word you do not know, a dictionary can tell you what the word means and how to say it.

> **dis•tort** (di stôrt´) *verb.* **1.** to twist the meaning of something. *The reporter* distorts *what people say.* **2.** to twist out of shape. *The mirror* distorts *my face when I look into it.*
>
> A phonetic spelling tells you how to say the word. Notice that *distort* is divided into two parts. Each part is called a **syllable.**
>
> The accent mark (´) after the second syllable shows you which syllable to stress when pronouncing the word.

Use the dictionary entry above to answer these questions.

1. Which meaning of *distort* do you find in the following sentence?

   Eduardo twisted the hanger and distorted its shape.

   a. Meaning #1   **b.** Meaning #2

2. True or false: *distort* has two syllables.

   a. true   **b.** false

3. Which is the correct way to say *distort*?

   a. di´ stôrt   **b.** di stôrt´

4. Use *distort* in a sentence of your own. Then write the number of the meaning you used.

   _____

   _____

   I used meaning # ____.

© Macmillan/McGraw-Hill

At Home: Have the student underline the words and phrases that helped him or her figure out each word's meaning.

The Astronaut and the Onion
Grade 4/Unit 1   **27**

Remember the following common spellings for the **long *i***
sound: *ie, i-e, igh, i,* and *y.*

Complete the following sentences with one of these long *i* words.

kind	drive	kite	wipe	pride	sky	prime
sly	sigh	fright	pies	spy	twice	find

1. The rocket rose up into the _____.

2. What _____ of person becomes an astronaut?

3. Fernando went outside on a windy day to fly his _____.

4. The spaceship orbited the moon not once, but _____.

5. The astronauts wanted to _____ life on Mars.

6. It's much easier to _____ a car than to pilot a spaceship.

Circle the word in each pair that has the long *i* sound.

7. fit   fight

8. dine   done

9. fleas   flies

10. rip   ripe

11. trim   try

12. high   hog

At Home: Challenge the student to think of words with the
long *i* sound. Then ask him or her to spell each word.

Fill in each blank with the correct vocabulary word.

raft	scattered	disgusted
downstream	cluttered	nuzzle

1. I'll never forget the first time I floated down a river on

   a _____.

2. The river rushed me _____.

3. On the side of the river, leaves were _____ here and there.

4. I passed a house. The front porch was _____ with old furniture and newspapers.

5. I saw a mother dog _____ her puppy.

6. I was _____ when I saw paper and cans in the water.

Write four more sentences about the end of this trip. Use an antonym of the words from the box in each sentence.

7. _____

   _____

8. _____

   _____

9. _____

   _____

10. _____

   _____

> The **characters** are the people, and sometimes animals, in a
> story. The **setting** is where and when a story takes place. The
> **plot** is what happens in the story.

At last we arrived at the ocean cottage. My brother and I were too
excited to look around the house. We ran out to explore the shore. There
were tide pools and seaweed, and minnows swimming in a tide pool.
When I stuck my hand in the water, the little fish darted under a piece of
seaweed. Farther down the rocky coast, we saw a seal resting on a rock!

My brother and I were so excited about seeing the seal that we had
a hard time falling asleep that night. The next morning we ran to find
the seal again. It was gone! But then we heard barking. In the shallow
water near the shore, a dark head looked at us, barked once again, and
disappeared below the water.

1. Name the setting of the passage.

_____

2. Who is the main character?

_____

3. What happens in the first part of the story?

_____

4. What important discovery do they make while they are exploring?

_____

5. How does the story end?

_____

At Home: Have the student think of a favorite story and
describe the setting in the story.

Name _____

As you read *The Raft,* fill in the Setting Flow Chart.

Setting

Event		Character's Reaction
	→	

Event		Character's Reaction
	→	

Event		Character's Reaction
	→	

How does the information you wrote in the Setting Flow Chart help you to analyze and make inferences about *The Raft*?

At Home: Have the student use the chart to retell the story.

Name _____

As I read, I will pay attention to the pace and tempo and try to match the action of the story.

	"Are we there yet?" Jamal asked, crossing his arms
9	across his chest.
12	"Almost, honey," his mom replied. "Look out the
20	window. Isn't it beautiful?"
24	Jamal didn't answer, but he did look. Out his mom's
34	window, all he could see was a rising, rocky cliff. Out his
46	own window, the cliff dropped down, and Jamal could see
56	the road winding below them. Below that were green
65	fields. A few houses and farms were **scattered** about.
74	The city was a long way away. It felt like they had been
87	driving forever.
89	They were driving up into the mountains to spend a
99	week at a ranch. His mom had lived at this ranch when
111	she was a little girl. "Some vacation," Jamal thought to
121	himself. 122

Comprehension Check

1. How does Jamal feel about his vacation? **Character, Setting, Plot**

2. How do you know that Jamal's mom probably enjoyed the ranch?
Character, Setting, Plot

	Words Read	−	Number of Errors	=	Words Correct Score
First Read		−		=	
Second Read		−		=	

At Home: Help the student read the passage, paying attention to the goal at the top of the page.

A **compass rose** shows north, south, east, and west. The **map key,** or **legend,** explains the symbols on the map.

Use the map to answer each question.

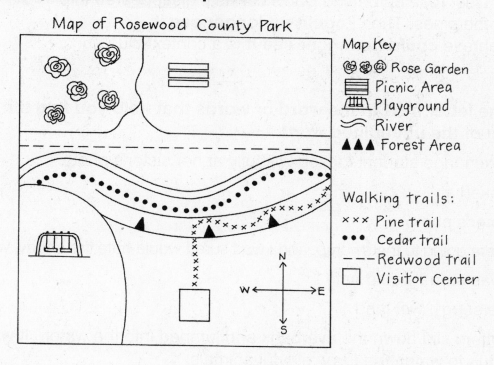

Map of Rosewood County Park

Map Key

Rose Garden
Picnic Area
Playground
River
Forest Area

Walking trails:
××× Pine trail
••• Cedar trail
--- Redwood trail
☐ Visitor Center

1. The picnic area is to the east of _____.

2. Which trail would you take to walk through the forest area?

_____

3. Can you take the Cedar trail to get to the Redwood trail? Explain.

_____

4. It is possible to get from the Visitor Center to the Rose Garden. What is

missing from the map? _____

At Home: Have the student make a map of a room in your house, using a map key with symbols and a compass rose.

The Raft
Grade 4/Unit 1

33

Sometimes you will find a word in a story that you do not know. Read the sentence the word is in, as well as the sentences around the word. They will often give a clue to its meaning.

Look for a clue to the meaning of *disappeared* below:
    Dust rose up behind Dad's car as it <u>disappeared</u> into the pines. Then I **could no longer see it.**
The phrase **could no longer see it** is a context clue.

Circle the letter next to the word or words that help you find the meaning of the underlined word.

1. The exchange student looked <u>wistfully</u> at her sister's photo.

   a. looked at

   b. sister's photo

2. We were going to the <u>swamp,</u> and I was sure I would hate the soggy, wet land.

   a. I was sure I would hate

   b. the soggy, wet land

3. The <u>otters</u> slid down the riverbank and jumped into the water. It was such fun to watch the furry, playful animals.

   a. slid down the riverbank

   b. furry, playful animals

4. I swam out to the <u>raft</u> and pulled myself up using the rope that held the logs together.

   a. the rope that held the logs together

   b. and pulled myself up

5. We paddled <u>upstream</u>, forcing our boat to move against the river's flow.

   a. paddled

   b. move against the river's flow

© Macmillan/McGraw-Hill

At Home: Find paragraphs in books and newspapers to read with the student. Use context clues to determine the meaning of any unfamiliar words.

Name _____

The long *o* sound can be spelled several different ways.

st<u>o</u>le (o_e)   f<u>oa</u>m (oa)   fl<u>ow</u> (ow)   m<u>o</u>ld (o)

Fill in the blanks using each long *o* word in the box once.

boat	close	floating	shallow	know
most	don't	home	soaked	go
rowed	owned	Cole	foal	hoped

1. We were _____ in our _____.

2. Along the bank we saw the _____ beautiful white horse.

3. I asked _____ if he knew who _____ her.

4. He answered, "I _____ _____."

5. Just then I caught sight of something small and brown and whispered,

   "She has a _____!"

6. "How _____ do you think we can get?" I asked.

7. I _____ to feed them the leftover apples from our lunch.

8. We _____ until the bottom scuffed against something
   below us and I stepped out to wade through the

   _____ water to shore.

9. To my surprise I promptly sank instead. I got _____!
   Cole thought it was hysterical!

10. "Let's _____ _____," I grumbled.

At Home: Take turns spelling long *o* words with the student.
See how many words you can come up with.

© Macmillan/McGraw-Hill

Name _____

A. Draw a line to match the vocabulary word to the word or words that mean the opposite.

Column 1

1. suspicious
2. silken
3. natural
4. protested
5. lumbering
6. scattered

Column 2

a. agreed willingly
b. dull and rough
c. trusting
d. moving gracefully
e. artificial
f. caused to go off in the same direction

B. Write the vocabulary word that has the same, or almost the same, meaning as the underlined word or words.

climate	accuse	journey	shimmer
roamed	paralyzed	completed	

1. The moon seemed to <u>shine faintly</u> in the sky. _____

2. He became <u>unable to move</u> with fear. _____

3. They <u>wandered</u> through the desert for days. _____

4. Finally, after two years, their <u>long trip</u> was over. _____

5. You can't <u>blame</u> him without any proof. _____

6. The <u>normal weather</u> in Siberia is cold and snowy. _____

7. When our work was <u>finished</u>, we returned home. _____

Now write a sentence of your own using two of the words in the box.

_____

A. Read each meaning. Write the vocabulary word in the puzzle grid.

Across

2. in the direction of the current

4. animals living in nature

6. moving in a clumsy manner

7. to touch or rub with the nose

8. careful thought

Down

1. having or showing good sense or sound judgment

3. proof

5. to hide in a sneaky manner

Name _____

| muttered | gaped | insult | snickering |
| legendary | fluke | flinched | |

Choose the correct word from the box to complete each sentence.

1. Jorge was angry because Tammy kept _____ when he struck out.

2. Jackie Robinson was a _____ baseball player. He was famous for his many skills.

3. When she missed the throw to first base, Danisha _____ quietly to herself.

4. I was so shocked when we won the baseball game that I

   _____ at my teammates in surprise.

5. When a baseball team wins by 12 runs, you hope it isn't just a

   _____.

6. I _____ when the ball came close to me.

7. Carla told Jefferson that he was a bad player. That was an

   _____.

Use three of the above words in sentences of your own.

8. _____

9. _____

10. _____

An author has a purpose when he or she writes. Usually authors write to **entertain,** to **inform,** or to **persuade**.

Read the passages and answer the questions.

Theo sat on the bench and watched as Molly went to bat. She took a big swing at the first pitch and missed. On the next pitch she surprised everyone and bunted the ball. It rolled slowly towards third base, and Molly sprinted to first. She got to first safely. Theo thought to himself, "Wow, that was pretty tricky. The fielders thought that she was going to hit the ball hard, so they weren't ready for that bunt. Maybe I could try that some time."

1. What was the author's purpose in writing this story? _____

2. What helped you decide on the author's purpose?

_____

_____

Jackie Robinson is a member of the Baseball Hall of Fame. Born in 1919 in Cairo, Georgia, Robinson went to college at the University of California in Los Angeles. He played baseball after college and became the first African American baseball player in the major leagues. He played for the Brooklyn Dodgers for ten years. During that time they won six pennants. Robinson stole home 19 times and was named the Most Valuable Player in 1949.

3. What was the author's purpose in writing the passage? _____

4. What helped you decide on the author's purpose?

_____

_____

🏠 **At Home:** Together, read passages from newspapers and magazines and decide on the author's purpose for writing them.

Name _____

As you read *Mighty Jackie*, fill in the Author's Purpose Map.

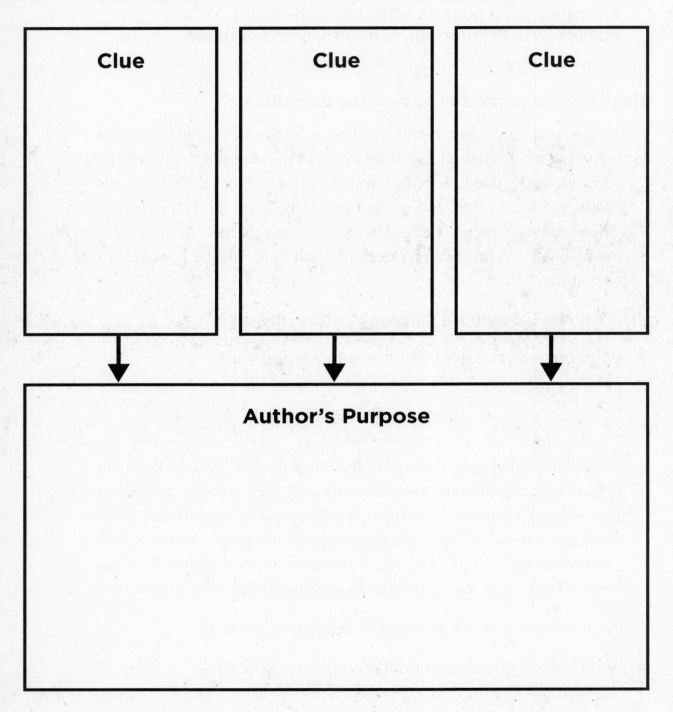

Clue	Clue	Clue

Author's Purpose

How does the information you wrote in the Author's Purpose Map help you to analyze and make inferences about *Mighty Jackie*?

At Home: Have the student use the chart to retell the story.

As I read, I will pay attention to pauses, stops, and intonation.

	Mildred Ella Didrikson was born on June 26, 1914, in
8	Port Arthur, Texas. Mildred's father built a gym for his
18	children in the backyard. The children played many sports,
27	including baseball. Mildred was a good hitter. So the boys
37	started calling her "Babe," after the **legendary** baseball
45	player Babe Ruth. Ruth was famous for hitting home runs.
55	It was no fluke that Babe Didrikson became a good athlete.
66	Babe's father read newspaper articles about the 1928
73	Olympic Games aloud to his children. Babe was 14 years
82	old at the time. She began to dream about competing in the
94	Olympics someday.
96	Babe attended high school during the late 1920s. She
104	excelled in every sport she tried. At only 5 feet (152 cm)
114	tall and 105 pounds (48 kg), Babe was small. But she was
124	strong. 125

Comprehension Check

1. Why does the author make it a point to explain Mildred Didrikson's nickname? **Author's Purpose**

2. How did Babe Didrikson's homelife help her to become an athlete? **Setting**

	Words Read	−	Number of Errors	=	Words Correct Score
First Read		−		=	
Second Read		−		=	

At Home: Help the student read the passage, paying attention to the goal at the top of the page.

Mighty Jackie
Grade 4/Unit 2

41

Name _____

> A **table** presents factual information—such as names, places, and numbers—in a compact form.

Look at the table from a sports almanac. Then use the table to answer the questions that follow.

The Top Five Pitchers in Baseball History

Name	Career Length	Games Won	Games Lost
Walter Johnson	21 years	417	279
Christy Matthewson	17 years	373	188
Sandy Koufax	12 years	165	87
Lefty Grove	17 years	300	141
Cy Young	22 years	511	316

1. What does this table tell you about these pitchers? _____

_____

2. Which of the pitchers had the shortest career? _____

3. Which pitcher won the most games? _____

4. Which pitcher lost the fewest number of games? _____

5. Which pitchers had careers that lasted the same number of years?

_____

6. Who scored highest in all three categories? _____

At Home: Create a table together that presents key facts about members of a favorite sports team.

When you come to a word you do not know in a passage, read the entire sentence. Other words in the sentence may give **clues** to the meaning of the unfamiliar word.

Circle the clue words in each sentence that help you figure out the meaning of the word in dark type.

1. The crowd was **stupefied** by how amazingly bad the team played.

2. The children were afraid of the **cantankerous** old man because he was angry and always yelled at them.

3. The whole-grain cereal was full of **nutrients** that keep athletes healthy.

4. Aldo hit the ball so hard that no one even saw the ball fly **swiftly** through the air.

5. The new stadium was so **colossal** that you could fit 80,000 people into it and still have tickets left over.

Write your own definitions for three of the words above. First write the word, then write what it means.

6. _____

7. _____

8. _____

At Home: Together, read a paragraph from a newspaper. Encourage the student to figure out the meaning of unfamiliar words from context clues.

Mighty Jackie
Grade 4/Unit 2

43

The letters **ch** and **tch** stand for the sound you hear in the following words.

| chopped | marching | each | pitcher | match |

Write the correct word on the line. Then circle the letters that make the *ch* sound.

1. I like to play _____ .

    a. coach   **b.** catch   **c.** cheat

2. Shannon wants to _____ her brother how to play baseball.

    a. chat   **b.** catcher   **c.** teach

3. The fans _____ when Tanika hits a home run.

    a. cheer   **b.** reach   **c.** hatch

4. There is _____ all around the baseball.

    a. inch   **b.** chin   **c.** stitching

5. Mario thinks there is too _____ talk about how he won the game.

    a. change   **b.** twitch   **c.** much

6. Write a silly sentence using words with *ch* and *tch*.

_____

_____

_____

At Home: Read a passage containing *ch* and *tch* words aloud to the student. Have the student identify the letters that name the sound.

Name _____

overheard	opportunities	boycotts	citizen
unions	strikes	border	

Choose the correct word from the box to complete each sentence.

1. Sometimes workers go on _____ to demand higher pay.

2. In America a _____ can vote to choose leaders in the government.

3. Some workers join _____ with other people who do the same job.

4. Mexico shares a _____ with the United States.

5. Robert _____ his parents whispering about their exciting plans for the new year.

6. People move from one country to another for different reasons, but all of them are looking for _____ to better their lives.

7. People will sometimes start _____ against companies and refuse to buy things from them.

Write sentences using three of the vocabulary words.

8. _____

9. _____

10. _____

Authors may not tell you everything about characters and events in a story. However, you need the information to understand the story. You can use clues to make **inferences**.

Sheila hopped and skipped to school. Today was the first day of school.

You know that Sheila is happy because she is hopping and skipping.

The yellow bus picked Xian up at the corner. He did not know anyone on the bus. He sat next to a girl in a red sweater. "Hi," she smiled. Xian knew the word and said *hi* back. "My name's Nancy." Xian just looked at her.

"Do you have Mr. Bellino this year?" Xian said nothing. "You're new, aren't you?" Xian bit his lip and stared at Nancy.

When the bus stopped, Nancy led Xian up the walk. "I'll show you around." Xian had a friend, and he gave Nancy a big smile.

Use the passage to answer the questions.

1. Where is Xian going? _____

2. How do you know where Xian is going?

_____

3. Why doesn't Xian answer some of Nancy's questions?

_____

4. How does Xian feel at the end of the passage? How do you know?

_____

At Home: Make up two related sentences and ask the student what inferences can be drawn from them. Trade places and make inferences from the student's sentences.

Name _____

As you read *My Diary from Here to There*, fill in the Inferences Word Web.

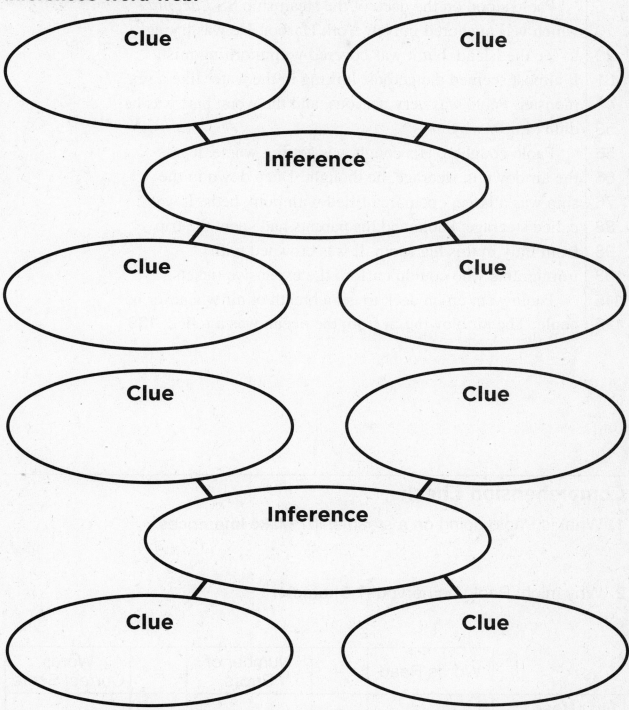

How does the information you wrote in the Inferences Word Web help you to generate questions about *My Diary from Here to There*?

At Home: Have the student use the chart to retell the story.

Name _____

As I read, I will pay attention to end punctuation in each sentence.

	Paolo stood on the deck of the steamship SS *Laconia,*
10	which was anchored in New York Harbor. He was trying
20	to see the island, but it was covered with morning mist.
31	It almost seemed dangerous, lurking in the water like a sea
42	monster. Paolo was very nervous, and the worst part was he
53	didn't know why.
56	Paolo coughed. His cough was getting worse. It was
65	the air down in steerage, he thought. Deep down in the
76	ship was a large, open area filled with bunk beds. It was
88	called steerage. Paolo and his parents had spent the trip
98	from Italy in this big room. It was crowded with
108	immigrants who couldn't afford the expensive tickets.
115	Paolo went up on deck to get a breath of air whenever he
128	could. The air blowing in from the ocean was a relief. 139

Comprehension Check

1. What is Paolo doing on a steamship? **Make Inferences**

2. Why might Paolo be nervous? **Character**

	Words Read	–	Number of Errors	=	Words Correct Score
First Read		–		=	
Second Read		–		=	

At Home: Help the student read the passage, paying attention to the goal at the top of the page.

Name _____

> A **primary source** is a first-person account of historical events told in letters, journals, or oral histories.

The following oral history was told by a woman named Sarah Thal. She settled in the United States in 1882. Read the story. Then answer the questions.

My husband had brothers in Milwaukee who sent home glowing reports of conditions in America. We wished to try our luck in that wonderful land. . . . We sailed from Antwerp and landed in Boston. I brought with me my linen chest, feather beds, pillows, bedding, etc. I have some bits of these things today. As most of the immigrants of that time were German, we reached Milwaukee without difficulty. Here my brother-in-law met us and took us to his home.

1. How can you tell the passage is a primary source?

_____

2. Give an example of the kind of information you find in the primary source that you would not find in another passage about moving to a new country.

_____

_____

3. How do you think Sarah felt about moving to America? Why?

_____

_____

4. How might an oral history by Sarah's brother-in-law be different from this one?

_____

_____

© Macmillan/McGraw-Hill

At Home: With the student, create a primary source about your life in your town or city. Use a letter or journal entry.

My Diary from Here to There
Grade 4/Unit 2

49

A dictionary sometimes tells you where a word comes from.
Knowing the **origin** of a word can help you understand it.
   mesa *noun.* a hill or mountain with a flat top
   word history: In Spanish the word *mesa* means "table."
How does the history help you understand the word?
You can picture how flat a mesa is by thinking of a table top.

jumbo *adjective.* very, very large. *word history:* comes from *Jumbo*, the name of a large elephant famous over 100 years ago
petroleum *noun.* an oily liquid found beneath Earth's surface. *word history:* comes from two Greek words meaning "rock" and "oil"
typhoon *noun.* a storm with violent winds. *word history:* comes from two Chinese words meaning "great wind"
zero *noun.* the number 0, which means no amount at all. *word history:* comes from an Arabic word that means "empty"

Use the dictionary entries above to answer the questions.

1. How does the word history of *jumbo* help you understand the word?

_____

_____

2. How does the word history of *typhoon* help you understand the word?

_____

3. How does the word history of *petroleum* help you understand the word?

_____

_____

4. How does the word history of *zero* help you understand the word?

_____

_____

At Home: If you have a dictionary at home, leaf through it together to find words with word histories. Then talk about them.

■ **Practice**

Phonics:
Words with *th, sh,
wh,* or *ph*

Name _____

> The letter pairs **sh, th, wh,** and **ph** have one sound, even
> though there are two letters in the pair. Say the following words
> aloud and listen to the one sound made by the letter pairs.
>
> • **th** <u>th</u>irty, bo<u>th</u>er
> • **sh** <u>sh</u>ove, wa<u>sh</u>er
> • **ph** <u>ph</u>rase, head<u>ph</u>one
> • **wh** <u>wh</u>irl, any<u>wh</u>ere

**Use the clues to fill in the blanks with words that have the *sh, ph,
wh,* or *th* sounds.**

1. I gave the money to my mother and _____.

2. I made a _____ before I blew out the candles on my
   birthday cake.

3. _____ is the library? Is it near Flower Street?

4. My camera helps me take good _____.

5. The _____ is a large and dangerous fish.

6. I'm going to the dentist because I have a cavity in one _____.

7. I picked up the _____ and called my friend.

8. I sailed home on a big _____.

9. I put the plates, forks, and knives into the _____ and
   turned it on.

10. I made a bar _____ to show the daily sales of my
    lemonade stand.

At Home: Have your child write a paragraph using new
words with *sh, th, ph,* or *wh.*

Name _____

temples   dynasties   heritage   preserve   overjoyed

Use the vocabulary words in the box to complete the sentences below.

1. Many people try to _____ beautiful old buildings.

2. The Han family was one of China's ruling _____.

3. The museum director was _____ when the police found the ancient statues.

4. People often gather in _____ to practice the rituals of their religions.

5. Many see ancient artwork as an important part of China's

_____.

Write sentences using three words from the list in the spaces provided.

6. _____

_____

7. _____

_____

8. _____

_____

> A **fact** is a statement you can prove. An **opinion** is a statement
> of belief that cannot be proved. Look for signal words such as
> *all, no one, probably, should,* and *everyone* to spot opinions.

**Suppose you are reading a magazine article about the looting of
treasures. Read each of the following statements and decide if it
is fact or opinion. Circle *Fact* or *Opinion* and write a sentence to
explain your answer.**

1. The looting of treasures should not be allowed.

   Fact   Opinion

   Explanation: _____

   _____

2. Looting is just human nature and will never stop.

   Fact   Opinion

   Explanation: _____

   _____

3. Police from many countries cooperate to stop the looting of treasures.

   Fact   Opinion

   Explanation: _____

   _____

4. No one would want to buy something that was stolen.

   Fact   Opinion

   Explanation: _____

   _____

© Macmillan/McGraw-Hill

At Home: Watch a television news report with the student.
Make statements to each other about it and decide whether
they are fact or opinion.

Stealing Beauty
Grade 4/Unit 2

53

Name _____

As you read *Stealing Beauty,* fill in the Fact and Opinion Chart.

Fact	Opinion

How does the information you wrote in the Fact and Opinion Chart help you to analyze and make inferences about *Stealing Beauty*?

At Home: Have the student use the chart to retell the story.

As I read, I will pay attention to tempo.

	Thousands of years ago in China, people made an
9	important discovery. They found out that caterpillars of
17	one kind of moth spin cocoons of silk. And better yet, they
29	found out that the cocoons could be unwound and the silk
40	thread could be woven into fabric.
46	Silk fabric is shiny. It is soft and smooth to the touch.
58	It is very light in weight. And it can be dyed in beautiful
71	colors.
72	For thousands of years, the Chinese were the only
81	people who knew how to produce silk cloth. People in
91	other countries wanted to trade for the precious silk
100	fabric. Traders traveled to and from China on one
109	main road. They traded goods such as spices, glass,
118	and gold for silk. Sometimes they even traded horses
127	for silk. Over time this route became known as the Silk
138	Road. 139

Comprehension Check

1. Are the statements in the second paragraph facts or opinions? **Fact and Opinion**

2. What is the main idea of the third paragraph? **Main Idea and Details**

	Words Read	–	Number of Errors	=	Words Correct Score
First Read		–		=	
Second Read		–		=	

At Home: Help the student read the passage, paying attention to the goal at the top of the page.

Name _____

Looking at the different parts of a book can help you figure out
if the book will have the information you need.

Front Cover	**Table of Contents**	**Index**
Title Page	**Glossary**	**Back Cover**

**Answer each question below by writing the name of the book
part in the space provided.**

1. Which two parts of a book tell you the title of the book and the name of

   its author? _____

2. Which two parts of a book include page numbers? _____

   _____

3. Where can you find a brief description of what the book is about?

   _____

4. Where could you find the meaning of a difficult word? _____

5. What part of a book tells you how many chapters are in the book?

   _____

6. Where would you look to find out quickly how much information on one

   topic is in the book? _____

At Home: Together, look at some of the student's books.
Discuss the different parts of each book.

Most nouns can be made plural in one of the following ways:
- add –*s*
- add –*es*
- if noun ends with a consonant and *y,* change *y* to *i* and add –*es*

Fill in each blank with the plural of the word written below.

1. People travel to _____ and _____ all over
   the world.   temple   church

2. There are _____ and greedy people in all
               looter

   _____ .
       country

3. Ancient _____ can be found in _____ .
            treasure   museum

4. People pass down _____ from _____ ago.
                     story   year

Write four sentences, each with a plural word. Use each kind of
plural at least once.

5. _____

   _____

6. _____

   _____

7. _____

   _____

8. _____

   _____

At Home: Ask the student to tell you the plural form of words
found in a newspaper or magazine.

Stealing Beauty **57**
Grade 4/Unit 2

> Some words begin with three consonants.
>
> (shr)imp   (thr)ash   (spr)out   (scr)amble   (spl)inter
>
> Listen to the sound the letters make. The sounds will help you recognize words that may seem unfamiliar.

Use three-consonant clusters, like those shown in the box, to create words that complete the following sentences.

1. As a social studies project, students dug up some mysterious objects

   from the old town dump and _____aped the dirt off them.

2. The students gently _____ubbed the objects.

3. They searched _____ough the library for books about their objects.

4. They came upon _____endid examples of old objects in the library books, but none showing the ones they had found.

5. Then one girl _____ieked because she had stumbled upon one of their finds.

6. Everyone _____ang to their feet to see the picture.

Write four sentences using *shr-, thr-, spr-, scr-,* and *spl-* words. You may continue with the story above or not.

7. _____

8. _____

9. _____

10. _____

At Home: With the student, find words that begin with the three-consonant clusters above. Keep a list and determine which combination you found most often.

© Macmillan/McGraw-Hill

Name _____

| hilarious | dizzy | nowadays | independence |
| handy | whirlwind | mischief | convinced |

Fill in the sentences below with words from the box. Then use the words in the blanks to complete the puzzle.

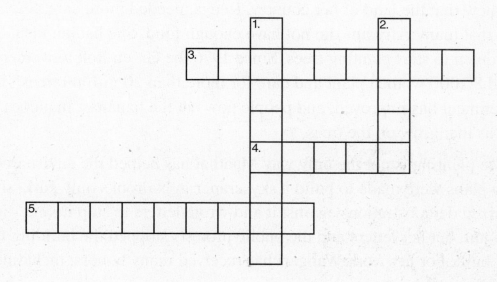

1. I never get into _____ when I'm inventing something!

2. But when success goes to my head, I feel _____!

3. Ideas come to me suddenly. They blow in like a _____.

4. My next invention will come in _____ for people who hate waiting.

5. I am _____ that I will make millions!

In both fiction and nonfiction stories, someone may face a **problem** then find a **solution,** or a way to solve it.

Read the passage. Then answer the questions that follow.

Wangari Maathai is an African woman who wanted to help her people. She knew that the land of her country, Kenya, needed more care. She also knew that many Africans did not have enough food. She had an idea. She got women to start planting trees. Since 1976 the Green Belt movement has helped 80,000 women plant and care for more than 20 million trees! The environment has improved, and people now eat the bananas, mangoes, and papayas that grow on the trees.

Tree planting is not the only way Maathai has helped the environment. When plans were made to build a skyscraper in Nairobi's only park, she organized demonstrations against it and wrote letters to stop it. She was put in jail, but her letters and the public protests stopped the building from being built. For her work Wangari has received many honors, including the Nobel Peace Prize.

1. Who is this passage about?_____

2. What is one problem Maathai faced?

_____

3. What other problem did Maathai face?

_____

4. What solution did she come up with?

_____

© Macmillan/McGraw-Hill

At Home: Together, read a story in a book or magazine. Ask what the problem and solution are.

As you read *How Ben Franklin Stole the Lightning,* fill in the
Problem and Solution Chart.

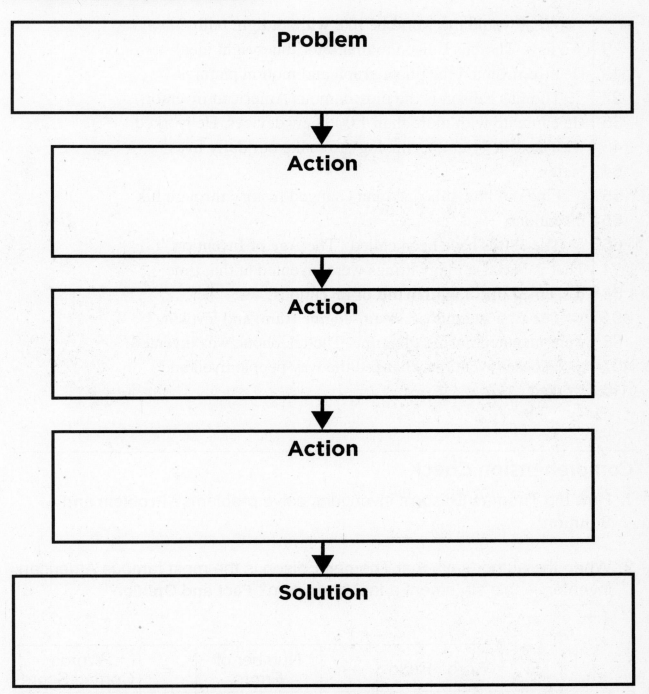

| **Problem** |
| **Action** |
| **Action** |
| **Action** |
| **Solution** |

How does the information you wrote in the Problem and Solution Chart help
you to generate questions about *How Ben Franklin Stole the Lightning*?

At Home: Have the student use the chart to retell the story.

How Ben Franklin Stole the
Lightning • **Grade 4/Unit 2**

61

As I read, I will pay attention to match my tempo with the energy of the passage.

	What would the world be like without light bulbs?
9	We have Thomas Edison to thank for that bright idea!
19	He also invented the phonograph and motion pictures.
27	Thomas Edison is the most famous American inventor.
35	He came up with more than 1,000 new devices. He worked
45	with electricity and technology to make our daily lives
54	better.
55	Find out how this one man changed history through his
65	inventions.
66	The 1800s have been called "The Age of Invention."
74	That is because many things were invented at that time.
84	It seemed like a **whirlwind** of inventions!
91	The first steamboat, steam-engine train, and airplane
98	were invented during this time. The telephone was invented
107	too. These inventions changed the way people lived and
116	worked. 117

Comprehension Check

1. How did Thomas Edison's inventions solve problems? **Problem and Solution**

2. When the author says that Thomas Edison is the most famous American inventor, is this statement a fact or opinion? **Fact and Opinion**

	Words Read	–	Number of Errors	=	Words Correct Score
First Read		–		=	
Second Read		–		=	

© Macmillan/McGraw-Hill

At Home: Help the student read the passage, paying attention to the goal at the top of the page.

Figurative language, such as metaphor and similes, uses words in fresh ways to suggest vivid images.
Metaphor: Sam is a tower of strength.
Simile: That man was as strong as a horse!
Alliteration is the repetition of the same first letter or consonant sound in a series of words. It was **B**lake's **B**lue **B**lanket.

Read the poem. Then circle or fill in the correct answer.

The wonderful wheel, which changed the world,
is as round as a ring and rolls and twirls
for carts and coaches,
cabbies and kings.
The wonderful wheel—oh, what bustle it brings!

1. What is this poem about?
   a. a wheel   **b.** a ring

2. Which words in the poem show alliteration?
   a. round, rolls, ring   **b.** twirls and changed

3. Which is a simile?
   a. carts and coaches   **b.** as round as a ring

4. What is simile a type of?
   a. alliteration   **b.** figurative language

5. What are the two reasons why "carts" was placed with "coaches" and

   "cabbies" was placed with "kings"? _____

   _____

   _____

   _____

At Home: Together, with your child, make up a phrase using words that all start with the same sound.

How Ben Franklin Stole the
Lightning • **Grade 4/Unit 2**

63

> **Idioms** are words or groups of words that cannot be
> understood by figuring out the meaning of each word. Example:
> pulling my leg. This group of words means "to trick or to tease."
> You can find this phrase in the dictionary under the word *leg.*

1. Under which word in the dictionary are you most likely to find this idiom?

   out of the blue _____

2. Read the sentence, then circle the meaning of "out of the blue."

   The news came *out of the blue*, so Isaac was shocked.

   a. suddenly   **b.** out of the sky

3. Use "out of the blue" in a sentence.

   _____

4. Read the sentence, then circle the meaning of "to wind up."

   The meeting was almost over when Janet said, "Let's *wind up* by
   six o'clock."

   a. change time on the clock   **b.** finish

5. Use "wind up" in a sentence.

   _____

Look up *wind up* in a dictionary. Write other meanings below.

6. _____

© Macmillan/McGraw-Hill

At Home: Together watch a television show and listen for
idioms. Talk about their meanings.

Sometimes when the letter r comes after a vowel, the sound of the short vowel changes. Say the following words aloud and notice the sound of the vowels.

bat   bar   cat   cart   fox   floor

The sounds of these vowels is shown as /är/ and /ôr/.

Circle the word with /är/ or /ôr/ to complete each sentence. Then write /är/ or /ôr/ on the blank at the end.

1. Please close the _____ when you leave. _____

   dear   door   dare

2. The _____ used watercolors to finish his painting. _____

   roar   rear   artist

3. The _____ on the rosebush are sharp. _____

   horns   thorns   stars

4. Ben Franklin's inventions _____ still in use today. _____

   care   core   are

5. We are going to have a birthday _____. _____

   party   pat   trap

6. My new scarf is nice and _____. _____

   warm   calm   pretty

At Home: Have the student look for /är/ and /ôr/ words in a book or magazine and write down the words he or she finds.

| apologize | genuine | harmless | cardboard |
| slithered | ambulance | weekdays | |

Use the correct vocabulary word from the box to fill in the blank.

1. On our hike a snake _____ across the trail.

2. The reptile exhibit at the zoo is open _____ from 10 A.M. to 5 P.M.

3. My encyclopedia says that the green snake we saw in my garden is

   _____.

4. An _____ rushed the snakebite victim to the hospital.

5. Evan should _____ for leaving a rubber snake on his sister's pillow.

6. The box I used for my snake's house was made of _____ and decorated with hearts and flowers.

7. Danielle's snake is _____, not rubber!

Write a sentence using one of the vocabulary words.

8. _____

   _____

Name _____

> Sometimes you have to use clues and what you know from your own experiences to help you **make inferences** about what's happening in a story.

Read the story. Then make inferences to answer the questions.

Evangeline didn't look up from her book when the new student said hello. The book was called *Adventures with Reptiles*. She'd already read it twice, but she just couldn't put it down. At the end of a chapter, she finally looked up from her book.

"I have that book," Jae said. "It's great. Do you want to come over after school to meet my pet lizard?"

"You bet!"

1. How does Evangeline feel when Jae says hello? How do you know?

_____

_____

2. Is the book Evangeline is reading one of her favorites? Why or why not?

_____

_____

3. What kinds of books would the new student like to read? How do you

know? _____

_____

4. Do you think Evangeline and the new student will become friends? Why

or why not? _____

_____

At Home: Watch a TV show with the student. Share any inferences you can make about the characters while watching.

Dear Mr. Winston
Grade 4/Unit 2

67

As you read Dear Mr. Winston, fill in the Inferences Word Web.

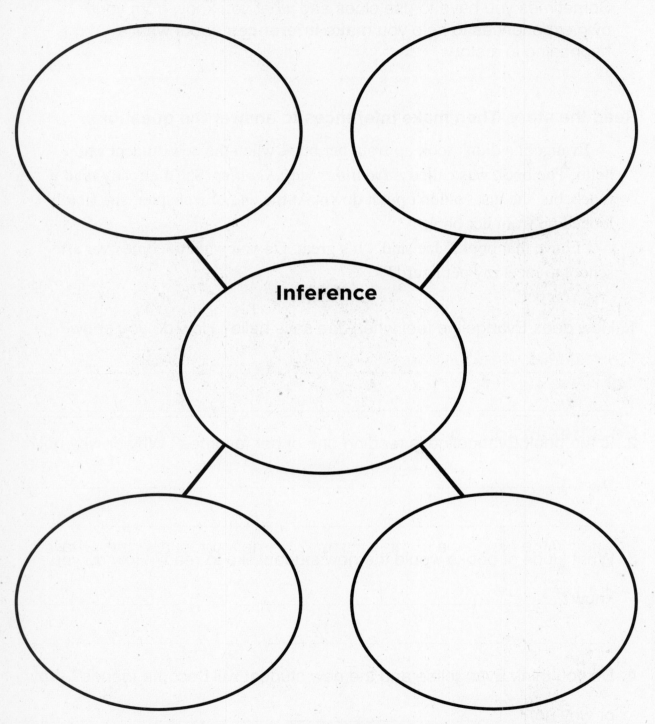

Inference

How does the information you wrote in the Inferences Word Web help you to generate questions about *Dear Mr. Winston*?

© Macmillan/McGraw-Hill

At Home: Have the student use the chart to retell the story.

As I read, I will pay attention to tempo.

	North America is a large area of land. It contains
10	many different climates and landscapes. Most of Mexico
18	and the southwestern United States is hot and dry. Other
28	areas, including the northeastern states and parts of Canada,
37	are cool and wet. Some areas have large mountain ranges,
47	like the Rocky Mountains in the West. Others have flat,
57	rolling plains, like the Midwest.
62	Snakes can be found in just about all of these places.
73	Snakes live in forests, canyons, and deserts. One might
82	even be living in your own backyard. Most snakes don't do
93	well in the cold. In fact, the hardy garter snake is the only
106	serpent that can survive in Alaska.
112	North America has five snake families. Two of these
121	families are poisonous, and three are not. Meet the five
131	families. As you read this book, you will get to know them
143	a lot better. 146

Comprehension Check

1. Make an inference about how snakes have adapted to their environments.
Make Inferences

2. What is the main idea of this passage? Name three supporting details.
Main Idea and Details

	Words Read	–	Number of Errors	=	Words Correct Score
First Read		–		=	
Second Read		–		=	

At Home: Help the student read the passage, paying attention to the goal at the top of the page.

An encyclopedia is a set of books with information on a wide variety of topics. An **electronic encyclopedia** has the same information but it is on a CD-Rom. You can use the **toolbar** to find the information you want.

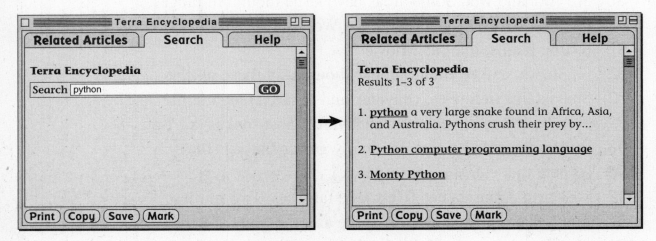

Study the pages above to answer these questions.

1. What information is the computer user looking for? _____

   _____

2. How many entries are shown for *python* in the encyclopedia?

   _____

3. Which button on the toolbar should the user click on to print out a copy of

   the page? _____

4. If you are looking for a good map of Australia, what button on the toolbar

   would you click? _____

5. If you are looking for more information about snakes, what button would

   you click? _____

At Home: Look at the second screen and discuss why the keyword *python* brings up such different results.

Prefixes and **suffixes** can be added to a word. The original word is called the **base word.** If you know what the base word is, you can figure out the meaning of the word with a prefix or suffix. You can find the meaning of prefixes and suffixes in a dictionary.

unhappy
The base word is **happy.** It means "feeling good."
The prefix *un-* means "the opposite of."
The word **unhappy** means "not feeling good."

Circle the base word in the sentence. Then tell what the word with the suffix or prefix means.

1. The snake's markings were colorful, with red and blue bands.

_____

2. Even small snakes can be dangerous sometimes.

_____

3. Knowing that the snake was hidden somewhere in the room made us all uncomfortable.

_____

4. The water moccasin swam under Khalid's boat and disappeared.

_____

5. Casey was successful in finding a picture of a rattlesnake in the book.

_____

At Home: Look through books to find words with prefixes and suffixes. Decide what the base word means, then decide what the word with the prefix or suffix means.

Dear Mr. Winston
Grade 4/Unit 2

71

> Some parts of words that are spelled differently are pronounced the same.
> **air** and **are:**   l<u>air</u>   bl<u>are</u>
> **ear** and **ere:**   d<u>ear</u>   m<u>ere</u>

Read the following sentences. Circle the words in the sentences that have an *air/are* spelling. Then underline the words that have an *ear/ere* spelling.

1. Please put the rocking chair over here by the fire.

2. Ms. Delgado was sincere when she said that she wanted to get a pair of snakes to keep as pets.

3. Her earrings shone in the bright glare of the noonday sun.

4. Severe weather can sometimes force airports to close.

5. It has been nearly three months since Maria's father shaved his beard.

6. Doesn't Aunt Greta have the same hairdo that she did last year?

Write two sentences, each using two words with air/are spellings or ear/ere spellings.

7. _____

_____

8. _____

_____

At Home: Together, make up sentences that have two words with the same sound but different spellings.

A. For each word in Column 1 write the letter of its meaning in Column 2.

Column 1

1. preserve _____

2. muttered _____

3. convinced _____

4. handy _____

5. slithered _____

6. genuine _____

Column 2

a. grumbled

b. sincere

c. persuaded

d. protect from harm

e. moved like a snake

f. useful

B. Answer each question with a sentence that includes the underlined word.

7. When was the last time you <u>gaped</u> at something?

_____

8. What happened the last time someone <u>flinched</u>?

_____

9. Why would someone be proud to be a <u>citizen</u> of the United States?

_____

_____

10. What <u>opportunities</u> might you get from going to college?

_____

_____

C. Supply an answer using the vocabulary word in your response.

11. legendary   Name a person you admire and explain why.

_____

12. fluke   Write about something that will never happen again.

_____

13. mischief   What might a puppy do if left alone?

_____

14. weekdays   What activities do you have after school?

_____

15. overjoyed   Tell about a time you felt extremely happy.

_____

D. Write a word from the list that has the same meaning as the underlined word or words.

> harmless   overheard   snickering   cardboard   hilarious

16. I saw her <u>laughing</u> behind his back. _____

17. I <u>learned</u> the other team's plays for Saturday's game at the library today.

They didn't know I was sitting right behind them! _____

18. My father told us the most <u>extremely funny</u> story. _____

19. Don't worry, that snake is <u>not able to hurt you</u>. _____

20. My notebook cover is made out of <u>thick, stiff paper</u>. _____

Name _____

| interfere | guardian | awkward |
| agile | proclaimed | tottered |

Use the context clues in each sentence to help you decide which vocabulary word fits best in the blank.

Small Snake couldn't move like the other snakes. "I'm so

_____," he cried.

Caterpillar offered to lend Small Snake a few legs. The young reptile

stumbled and _____ on them.

Raven stuck out her chest and _____, "I am the one who

can make this poor snake _____ enough to slither here and

there."

Mr. Caterpillar offered to help, but Raven waved him away and said,

"Do not _____ with what I am doing."

She made a straight line of poles in the ground. "Now,
go in and out from each pole to the next."

Small Snake found that he was curving and slithering.
"I know how to do it now!" he cried.

Raven said, "Caterpillar, you will watch out for

Small Snake and be his _____ until he
grows up."

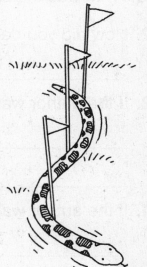

When authors write, they have a **purpose,** or reason, for what they want their work to do. They write fiction to **entertain.** They write nonfiction to **inform.** And they write essays to **persuade.**

Read the story excerpt below and decide on the author's purpose.

Squirrels did not always have big, bushy tails. Once upon a time, they had long, pointed tails, which did nothing to help them balance high up in the trees. Squirrels had to move slowly and were always afraid of falling. Also, they had to remember to hold up their tails or the scales that covered them would scrape against the tree bark and let predators know where they were.

Armadillos, on the other hand, had very bushy tails, but it was difficult to tuck all that lovely fur in when they had to roll up in protective little balls.

1. What was the author's purpose in writing this story? _____

2. How did you decide on the author's purpose? _____

_____

3. If the author wanted to inform readers, what would the author write?

_____

_____

4. If the author wanted to persuade readers, what would the author write?

_____

_____

© Macmillan/McGraw-Hill

At Home: Pick a word such as *dog, eating,* or *feet.* Use the word to make up a brief passage that entertains, informs, or persuades.

As you read *Roadrunner's Dance*, fill in the Author's Purpose Map.

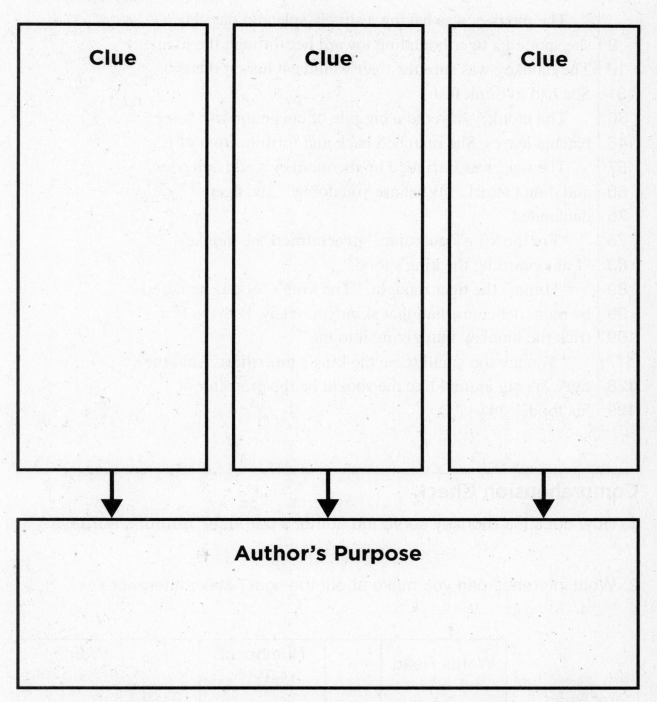

Clue	Clue	Clue

Author's Purpose

How does the information you wrote in the Author's Purpose Map help you to evaluate *Roadrunner's Dance*?

At Home: Have the student use the chart to retell the story.

Name _____

As I read, I will pay attention to pauses, stops, intonation, and the characters' words.

	The monkey was having a simply splendid day. Then
9	she spotted a tiger bounding toward her through the jungle.
19	The monkey was sure the tiger would eat her on the spot.
31	She had to think fast.
36	The monkey covered a big pile of coconuts with some
46	banana leaves. She marched back and forth in front of it.
57	The tiger was intrigued by the monkey's odd behavior
66	and didn't attack. "What are you doing?" the tiger
75	demanded.
76	"I'm the king's guardian," **proclaimed** the monkey.
83	"I am guarding the king's food."
89	"Hmm," the tiger thought. "The king's food is bound to
99	be more delicious than that skinny monkey. Perhaps I can
109	trick the monkey into giving it to me."
117	"You are too small to be the king's **guardian**," said the
128	tiger. "A big animal like me should be the protector of
139	his food." 141

Comprehension Check

1. How does the monkey serve the author's purpose? **Author's Purpose**

2. What inference can you make about the tiger? **Make Inferences**

	Words Read	−	Number of Errors	=	Words Correct Score
First Read		−		=	
Second Read		−		=	

At Home: Help the student read the passage, paying attention to the goal at the top of the page.

- **Foreshadowing** is the use of clues to hint at what is going to happen.
- **Symbolism** is the use of an object to represent an idea.

Read each passage. Then on the blank line, indicate whether the passage had any examples of *symbolism* or *foreshadowing*. Explain your answer.

1. Yoko thought again about her dream. It was such a strange dream. In it, she was feeling confused, as if her thoughts were far away. Then an enormous yellow rhinoceros charged her from the left and almost trampled her.

    Stepping off the curb to cross the avenue, Yoko wondered what her dream meant. Suddenly she heard a blaring horn and the screech of brakes. Yoko looked to her left and saw the school bus. She jumped back to safety.

    _____

    _____

2. Sheriff Crawford reached for his cowboy hat and looked his deputy in the eye. "If Jed and his gang are headed this way, I plan to head them off at the pass. Round up the boys and meet me there."

    "But how will we know that it's Jed, Sheriff?" Barney asked.

    "He always wears a mask that covers his whole face and rides a troublesome horse."

    _____

    _____

© Macmillan/McGraw-Hill

At Home: Help the student write a story that contains foreshadowing or symbolism.

Roadrunner's Dance
Grade 4/Unit 3

79

A **synonym** is a word that means the same or almost the same as another word. For example, a synonym for *guardian* is *protector.*

Replace each of the words in parentheses with one of the following synonyms.

| clumsy | nimble | announced | meddle | wobbled |

1. "Don't (interfere) _____ with my plans to be king of the road!"

2. The roadrunner was (awkward) _____ when he first tried to run and jump.

3. He (tottered) _____, but he did not fall.

4. Later, when Roadrunner danced in circles, you could see how (agile)

   _____ he had become.

5. "Roadrunner is our hero!" the animals (proclaimed) _____.

Write a sentence using a synonym for both of the words in dark type.

6. **frightened** and **trembled** _____

   _____

7. **yelled** and **bragged** _____

   _____

8. **hopped** and **quick** _____

   _____

© Macmillan/McGraw-Hill

At Home: Give each other a list of words and ask for synonyms.

> The /ûr/ sound can be spelled **er, ir, ur,** and **ear.** The sound is found in words such as **serpent, bird, turkey,** and **heard.**

Underline the *vowel + r combination* that represents the /ûr/ sound in each of these words.

1. b u r d e n
2. s t e r n l y
3. s e r p e n t
4. b i r t h
5. t u r n i p

6. w h i r l w i n d
7. l e a r n e r
8. p u r p o s e
9. p e r s o n
10. p e a r l

Now read the paragraph below. Find and circle six words that have the /ûr/ sound. Then continue the story. Circle the words with the /ûr/ sound.

One day, a raccoon climbed in the window of a house. He found a pearl necklace on the floor. Holding it carefully in his mouth, he took it outside. Then he returned and carried away a small purse. Finally, he emerged with a purple shirt.

_____

_____

_____

_____

_____

© Macmillan/McGraw-Hill

🏠 **At Home:** Read a page from a newspaper or magazine together. Challenge the student to find as many words as possible that contain the /ûr/ sound.

Roadrunner's Dance
Grade 4/Unit 3

81

| injustice | ancestors | unfair | avoided |
| numerous | unsuspecting | segregation | |

Use the clues below to complete the vocabulary word puzzle.

Across

1. kept away from
5. not aware, not expecting
7. unjust, unreasonable

Down

2. unfairness, an unjust act
3. people from whom one is descended
4. the practice of separating one racial group from another
6. many

> Authors write stories and plays to **entertain.** They write articles
> and books to **inform.** When authors write to **persuade,** they
> give reasons for their point of view, which is what the authors
> believe and want you to believe, too. What they write is not
> always backed up by facts.

**Read the following sentences. Think about the author's purpose.
After each sentence write *inform* or *persuade.***

1. In the South before 1955, African-American people had to drink from

   water fountains labeled "Colored Only." _____

2. Laws that separated African Americans from other Americans were

   unjust and should never have been made. _____

3. People should rise up and demand justice when they are treated unfairly.

   _____

4. You need to keep hope alive by believing in yourself and in a better

   world. _____

5. In 1955, Rosa Parks was arrested for refusing to give up her seat near

   the front of a bus. _____

**Write a sentence to persuade readers to support your point of
view on a topic you feel strongly about.**

_____

_____

_____

At Home: Have the student write two sentences about the
same topic: one intended to inform and one intended to
persuade.

My Brother Martin **83**
Grade 4/Unit 3

Name _____

As you read *My Brother Martin,* fill in the Author's Purpose Map.

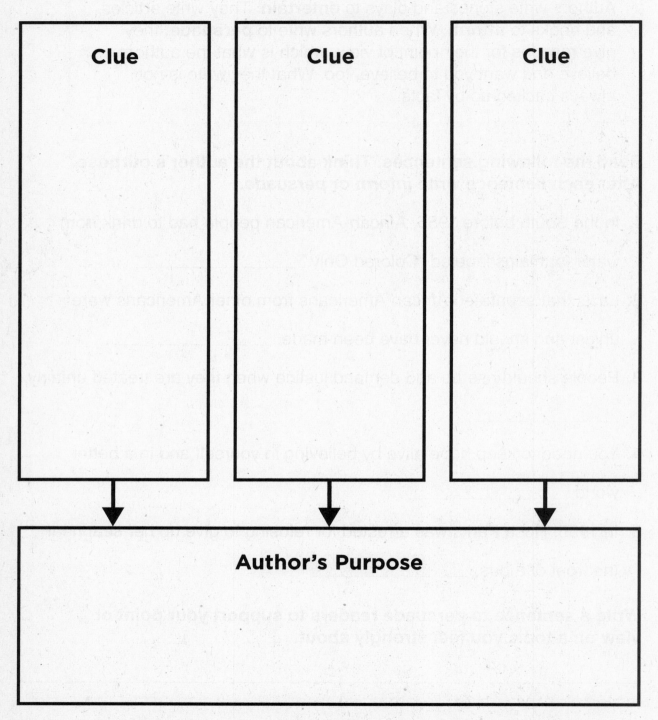

Clue	Clue	Clue

Author's Purpose

How does the information you wrote in the Author's Purpose Map help you
to evaluate *My Brother Martin?*

At Home: Have the student use the chart to retell the story.

© Macmillan/McGraw-Hill

Name _____

As I read, I will pay attention to punctuation in each sentence.

	Coretta Scott King never planned on being a civil rights
10	leader. She thought she would become a teacher or a singer.
21	Instead, she became a leader in the fight for equal rights.
32	Coretta Scott was born in 1927 in a small town in
42	Alabama. She walked three miles to get to school each
52	morning. And she walked three miles back each afternoon.
61	Every day she watched school buses drive white children to
71	their school.
73	In those days **segregation** was the law in the South.
83	African Americans could not go to certain restaurants.
91	They could not drink from certain water fountains. They
100	had to sit in the back of public buses. Black children and
112	white children went to separate schools.
118	Coretta's father Obadiah (oh-buh-DIGH-uh) was the
123	first African American in his county to own his own truck.
134	Some white truckers felt that he was taking away their
144	business. One day the Scotts came home from church to
154	find that their home had burned down. 161

Comprehension Check

1. Is the author's purpose to persuade? If not, what is the author's purpose?
Author's Purpose

2. Why do you think the Scotts' house was burned down? **Make Inferences**

	Words Read	−	Number of Errors	=	Words Correct Score
First Read		−		=	
Second Read		−		=	

At Home: Help the student read the passage, paying attention to the goal at the top of the page.

Letters have specific formats, but they all have the same three parts.
- A **salutation** is the line in the letter in which the writer greets the person to whom it was written.
- The **body** of the letter is the main part of the letter, containing the writer's message.
- The **complimentary closing** is the line above where the writer signs his or her name.

Read the letters below. Identify each part by drawing a line to the correct label below. On the blank, write whether it is a business or a personal letter.

7325 Hastings Road
San Diego, CA 90124
October 17, 2008

Hi, Jamal and Linda,

It was awesome to see you guys last week! The food was great and the company couldn't be beat.

Thanks again for having me over for the weekend. Next time, it's my turn.

Love,
Erica

_____

Body

Salutation

Complimentary Closing

7325 Hastings Road
San Diego, CA 90124

October 20, 2008

Levinson Randall, Inc.
62941 Chuckwalla Way
El Paso, TX 79901

Attn: Ms. Ann Gregory, Customer Service

Dear Ms. Gregory:

I am sending this letter to inform you that two of the four vases I ordered arrived damaged due to poor packaging.

Kindly send me two more of the Ballymoney crystal vases as soon as possible, and let me know how I should return the broken vases to you.

Sincerely,

Erica Eliades

_____

At Home: Together, write a personal and a business letter, using the models above. Have the student make sure the letters have a salutation, a body, and a complimentary closing.

> The prefix **un-** means "not."   **Unfair** means "not fair."
> The prefix **re-** means "again."   **Retell** means "tell again."

Circle the phrases in the story that would sound better using the prefixes *un-* or *re-*. Then write the new words below.

"It's terribly not fair, Grandmother!" Cordelia exclaimed. "Wilson School is just three blocks away. Why can't I just keep attending my classes there?"

Cordelia's grandmother looked at the bowl of cold, not eaten soup and left Cordelia's question not answered. "Let me warm again that pea soup for you, honey. You'll feel better after you have had your dinner."

"I know you do not like this, Grandmother. Even though you're not saying anything, I know you're terribly not happy with the new laws. So, why can't you admit that scheduling again our classes miles away is not acceptable!"

Cordelia looked over her glasses at her granddaughter. "No use talking about it around our kitchen table, child. But there will be talk all over this great land of ours. And mark my words, Cordelia, these not fortunate days will not go not noticed."

_____   _____

_____   _____

_____   _____

_____   _____

_____   _____

At Home: Together, read from a newspaper, magazine, or book. Ask the student to identify and define words that begin with the prefixes *re-* and *un-*.

My Brother Martin
Grade 4/Unit 3

87

Say these words aloud:

knives   plum**b**er   ca**l**m   **w**riggle

In these words, the letter in dark type is silent.

Quietly read the sentences aloud to yourself. Then circle the letter in the underlined word that you did not pronounce.

1. Rosa Parks <u>knew</u> that staying in her seat was the right thing to do.

2. Taking a risk might make the <u>palms</u> of your hands sweaty.

3. Christine <u>kneeled</u> down on the floor to pick up the paper she had dropped.

4. Martin's father needed a <u>wrench</u> to fix the piano bench.

5. The <u>tombs</u> in the cemetery remind us of those who came before us.

Using a dictionary, find at least 5 other words that begin with *kn* and *wr*. Write these words on the lines below and circle the silent letter in each one.

     kn- **words**   *wr-* **words**

_____   _____

_____   _____

_____   _____

_____   _____

_____   _____

© Macmillan/McGraw-Hill

At Home: Read passages together and ask the student to identify words with silent letters and pronounce them.

Name _____

| identified | enterprising | persistence | venture |

Fill in the vocabulary word for each sentence. Write the numbered letter in the mystery word below.

1. Gary worked in the garden, sold newspapers, and created an Internet

   page. He is a very __ __ __ __ __ __ __ __ __ __ __ person.

                                         1

2. Gina's idea to sell vegetables in farm country is a risky

   __ __ __ __ __ __ __.
           2

3. After six years of farming, Kinesha keeps trying to reach her goal. She

   has a lot of determination and __ __ __ __ __ __ __ __ __ __ __.
                               5   6   3

4. Tessa __ __ __ __ __ __ __ __ __ __ the stray dog. It lived with the
             4

   family three houses away from her.

5. Find the missing letter for the Mystery Word in the word DEDICATED.

   __

6. MYSTERY WORD:

   __ __ __ __ __ __
    1 2 3   4 5 6

When you **compare** two or more things, you are looking for how they are similar. When you **contrast** two or more things, you are looking for how they are different.

Words that Signal a Comparison		
alike	each	similar
also	in addition to	too
both	same	

Words that Signal a Contrast		
different	in contrast	separately
but	while	opposite
on the other hand	instead	
however	separate	

Write whether you think each sentence below is part of a *comparison* or a *contrast*. Circle the word or words that you base your answer on.

1. Jennifer and Jeffrey were twins, but they had very different ideas about

   how to run a business. _____

2. Monique's second business was also quite successful. _____

3. Both of the students have their own business. _____

4. The first job David had was boring; on the other hand, his second job

   was interesting. _____

5. Walking dogs was fun, while mowing lawns was hard. _____

6. Keisha liked spending; however, Julie wanted to save. _____

7. Sandy and Pedro mowed lawns and were alike in the way they treated

   their customers. _____

8. Pedro worked on weekends instead. _____

© Macmillan/McGraw-Hill

At Home: Pick two items in your house and ask the student to compare and contrast them.

As you read *Kid Reporters at Work*, fill in the Venn Diagram.

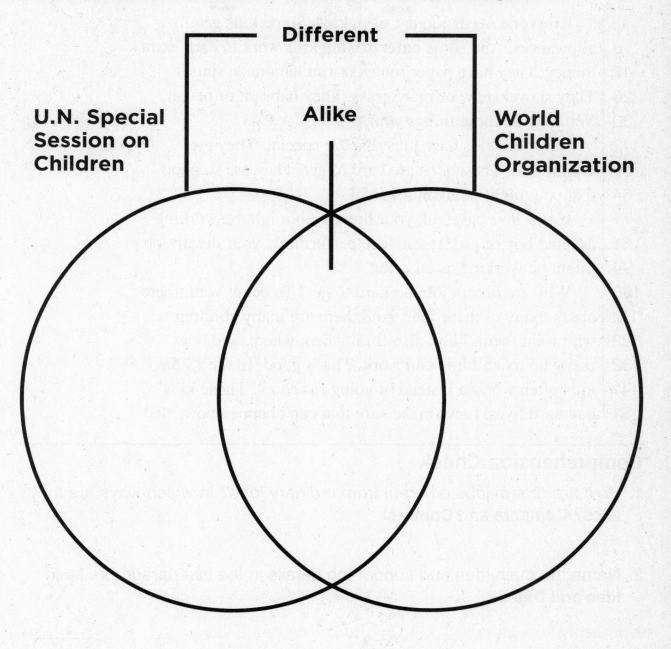

Different

**U.N. Special
Session on
Children**

Alike

**World
Children
Organization**

How does the information you wrote in the Venn diagram help you to summarize *Kid Reporters at Work*?

At Home: Have the student use the chart to retell the story.

Kid Reporters at Work
Grade 4/Unit 3

91

As I read, I will pay attention to tempo.

	Everyone needs money, even kids. Some kids get
8	allowances. And some **enterprising** kids work to earn extra
17	money. They have paper routes or run lemonade stands.
26	They shovel snow or mow grass. They baby-sit or pet-sit.
36	You may do these things yourself.
42	But some kids have jobs that are special. They are
52	dream jobs. These jobs are hard to get. They are so good
64	that you might do them for free!
71	If you love baseball, your dream job might be working
81	as a bat boy or girl. If you love performing, your dream job
94	might be working as an actor.
100	Why are dream jobs so hard to get? To begin with, there
112	aren't many of these jobs. And there are many children
122	who want them. Laws also limit when, where, and how
132	many hours children can work. That's good. In the 1800s,
141	kids often worked instead of going to school. Those kids
151	had hard lives. Laws make sure that can't happen now. 161

Comprehension Check

1. How are dream jobs different from ordinary jobs? In which ways are they alike? **Compare and Contrast**

2. Name the main idea and supporting details in the last paragraph. **Main Idea and Details**

	Words Read	−	Number of Errors	=	Words Correct Score
First Read		−		=	
Second Read		−		=	

© Macmillan/McGraw-Hill

At Home: Help the student read the passage, paying attention to the goal at the top of the page.

You can search for a book in a library's electronic card catalog by subject, author, or title. The books you find will show up in a screen that looks something like this.

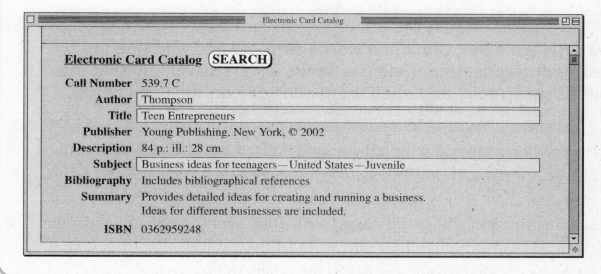

Electronic Card Catalog (SEARCH)

Call Number 539.7 C
Author Thompson
Title Teen Entrepreneurs
Publisher Young Publishing, New York, © 2002
Description 84 p.: ill.: 28 cm.
Subject Business ideas for teenagers—United States—Juvenile
Bibliography Includes bibliographical references
Summary Provides detailed ideas for creating and running a business. Ideas for different businesses are included.
ISBN 0362959248

Circle the correct information from the card-catalog card above.

1. The title of the book is:

   Young Publishing   Teen Entrepreneurs

2. The author of the book is:

   Thompson   Young

3. The library location for this book is:

   539.7 C   0362959248

4. In what year was the book published?

   539.7 C   2002

Read the summary on the card to answer the question.

5. Would this book help you find ideas for classroom projects? Why?

_____

At Home: Talk about the library card and what each item means.

Kid Reporters at Work
Grade 4/Unit 3

93

Different verbs follow different rules for adding **-ed** and **-ing**

seemed	admitted	arriving
obeyed	carried	answering

Read the passage. Circle the words with *-ed* and *-ing* that are spelled correctly. Underline the words with *-ed* and *-ing* that are spelled incorrectly and spell them correctly on the lines below.

Lateesha, Toby, and Margarita decideed to start buying notebooks for seventy cents and selling them for a dollar a book. Lateesha was in charge of geting the notebooks. Toby was supposed to make signs telling everyone about their sale. Margarita was investigatieng where they could sell their books. Things did not go well. Toby kept forgeting to make the signs. Margarita couldn't get anyone to let them sell the books in school. Lateesha decided to quit and beged the others to forgive her.

Toby and Margarita told Lateesha that they were clossing the notebook business and openning a dog wash instead. They hurryed to the store to buy soap and towels. Margarita and Toby were hopping it would be a success. Lateesha was worryed, especially when she realizeed that their first customer was a Saint Bernard.

"Well, I've enjoied knowing you guys," Lateesha said.

1. _____   2. _____   3. _____

4. _____   5. _____   6. _____

7. _____   8. _____   9. _____

10. _____   11. _____   12. _____

© Macmillan/McGraw-Hill

At Home: Together, find verbs in books or magazines with the ending *-ed* or *-ing*. Ask the student how to spell the verb without the ending.

When the letters **c** and **g** are followed by **e, i,** or **y,** they usually have a soft sound. Say the following words aloud.

ceiling	circus	cycle
genius	giant	gyroscope

Circle the word with soft *c* or *g* and write it on the line.

1. The young people were _____ their plan would work.

   careful   certain   concerned

2. They wanted to work in the _____.

   city   country   crowd

3. They could help people exercise in a _____.

   gymnasium   grade school   gang

4. Or they could give _____ care to sick pets.

   glad   grateful   gentle

5. Maybe they could feed the pets _____.

   cereal   corn   cupcakes

6. They could play with the _____ while they were not working.

   game   goose   gerbil

7. They could make sure the animals were free of _____.

   grease   gags   germs

8. Shelby has been learning to play the _____.

   clarinet   cymbals   castanets

At Home: Have the student make a list of five soft *c* and five soft *g* words.

patchwork   mysterious   responsibility   midst
loosened   amazement   sores

Choose the correct vocabulary word from the list to complete the sentence. Write the words on the lines.

David had a dog. He knew it was his **1.** _____ to take care of Spot. Of course, they had fun together. They played and ran and

explored. Then one day, in the **2.** _____ of having fun, Spot ran through some poison ivy. He soon was covered with painful

3. _____. David took his dog home and washed Spot as best he could. To comfort Spot, David found an old

4. _____ quilt. He wrapped Spot up in it and sat with him on the porch. At first, Spot tried to scratch. Then a

5. _____ thing began to happen. Spot stopped wriggling and trying to scratch. David **6.** _____ the quilt and looked

at Spot's legs in **7.** _____.
They were still red and swollen. Somehow, having his owner take care of him had calmed him down.

Add a sentence to the passage.

8. _____

_____

_____

Name _____

> Recognizing the **sequence of events** helps you understand the order in which things happen in a story.

Read the passage below. Then number the sentences below to show the sequence of events.

The Plains Indians lived in North America before the Europeans came. Since they had no horses, the Plains Indians traveled on foot. To hunt buffalo, they would surround a herd and shoot the buffalo with bows and arrows.

This changed when Spanish explorers came to North America and brought horses with them. Now the Plains Indians hunters were able to ride horses and follow buffalo over long distances. They carried tipis with them and set up camps. The hunters could kill buffalo and pull them back to camp using their horses.

Later guns again changed the way that Plains Indians hunted.

1. _____ Spanish explorers brought horses to North America.

2. _____ The Plains Indians used horses and traveled long distances to hunt buffalo.

3. _____ The Plains Indians hunted buffalo on foot before the Europeans came to North America.

4. _____ The Plains Indians used guns to hunt buffalo.

Add an event to the paragraphs and tell where it belongs in the sequence of events.

_____

_____

At Home: Together, look at a book or a newspaper or magazine article and identify the sequence of events.

Mystic Horse
Grade 4/Unit 3

97

Name _____

As you read *Mystic Horse*, fill in the Sequence Chart.

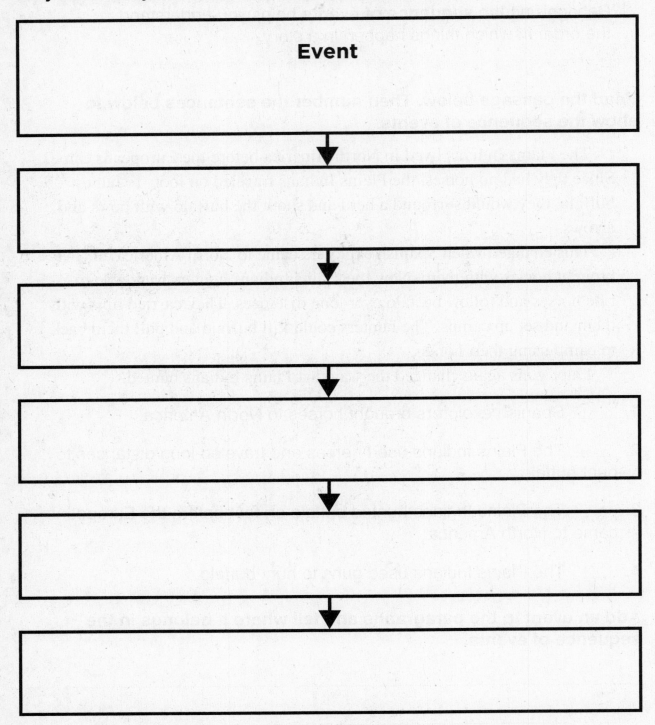

Event

How does the information you wrote in the Sequence Chart help you
to summarize *Mystic Horse*?

At Home: Have the student use the chart to retell the story.

Name _____

As I read, I will pay attention to tempo and match the energy and enthusiasm of the passage.

	But there came a time when many days of heavy rain
11	made the Quillayute River overflow. The houses washed
19	away. Then the Quileute moved to the prairies.
27	Not long after, the weather grew cold. The rain turned
37	into hail and sleet. The fishermen could not break through
47	the ice in the rivers to go fishing. Falling hailstones were
58	so big that people were killed. The people grew afraid to
69	go outside. They were running out of food. Men, women,
79	and children were becoming weak and sick.
86	At this time, the Great Chief of the Quileute called a
97	meeting of all the people in the tribe. He stood before them
109	in a **patchwork** shawl made up of buffalo skins stitched
119	together. The people begged the chief to do something. The
129	**responsibility** of watching over his people weighed heavily
137	upon him. "We will ask the Great Spirit who soars above
148	Earth for help," said the chief. 154

Comprehension Check

1. What were the events that caused the Great Chief of the Quileute to call a meeting? Name the events in the order in which they occurred. **Sequence**

2. What is the purpose of a legend such as this? **Author's Purpose**

	Words Read	–	Number of Errors	=	Words Correct Score
First Read		–		=	
Second Read		–		=	

© Macmillan/McGraw-Hill

At Home: Help the student to read the passage, paying attention to the goal at the top of the page.

You can find **online articles** on the Internet. Each online article has its own web address, or **URL.** In an article, clicking on underlined words, called **links,** takes you to other articles related to your topic. Larger articles can be broken up into several pages. If they are, clicking a link called **Next** will take you to the next page.

Read this excerpt from an online encyclopedia article about tepees. Then answer the questions that follow.

Tipis
by Kendra Lundquist

The <u>Plains Indians</u> lived in the area now called the Midwest. They built tipis for their homes. These were upside-down cone shapes, built with long poles. Animal skins were pinned and fastened to the outside of the cone, providing a roomy home. The Plains Indians made fires within the tipis. They were usually built in a small fireplace. The walls of the tent reflected the heat back into the middle of the tipi so that a small fire kept the tipi very warm in winter.

1. What is the title of the article that was found at this address? _____

2. What is the article about? _____

_____

3. What underlined link is part of the article? _____

4. What will happen if you click on the underlined link?

_____

_____

© Macmillan/McGraw-Hill

At Home: Create your own online article using the model at the top of the page.

Homophones are pairs of words that are pronounced the same but have different spellings and meanings.

here / hear	needed / kneaded	plains / planes
there / their	seen / scene	buries / berries
rain / rein	four / for	road / rode
blue / blew	through / threw	

Read the passage. Write *correct* on the lines below if the right homophone is used. If the wrong homophone is used, write the correct word on the line.

Some Native Americans lived on the <u>planes</u> in the middle of our country.
                                                1

The land <u>their</u> is beautiful. The sky is <u>blue</u> and tall grass seems to go on
              2   3

forever. Even today, the miles of grass are a beautiful <u>scene</u>. The Indians
                                                    4

<u>road</u> their horses <u>threw</u> the <u>plains</u> hunting <u>four</u> buffalo to eat. They also ate
  5   6   7   8

<u>berries</u> and nuts to add to <u>there</u> diet. It was a hard life but the Indians were
  9   10

proud of the life they lived.

1. _____

2. _____

3. _____

4. _____

5. _____

6. _____

7. _____

8. _____

9. _____

10. _____

At Home: Look at words in books or magazines and see if you can find homophones.

Mystic Horse
Grade 4/Unit 3

101

Plurals are formed in the following ways:

- Most plural words end in *-s.*
- When a word ends in *s*, *-es* is added to make the plural.
- When words end in *e*, the *e* is dropped and *-es* is added.
- When a word ends in *y,* the *y* is dropped and *-ies* is added.

Write the correct plural form of the underlined word on the line.

1. The <u>horse</u> _____ of the Plains Indians carried their belongings.

2. The men carried <u>arrow</u> _____ to hunt for buffalo.

3. They sometimes suffered <u>loss</u> _____ when a buffalo attacked.

4. The buffalo herds had thousands of acres to roam in and eat the different

   <u>grass</u> _____ on the plains.

5. The Indians ate <u>berry</u> _____ as part of their diet.

6. When in camp, the Indians built <u>fire</u> _____ in their tipis to
   keep warm.

7. They moved their <u>camp</u> _____ when food became scarce.

8. The Plains <u>Indian</u> _____ were proud people.

At Home: Play a plurals game. Write down a noun and have
the student write the plural. Then trade roles.

© Macmillan/McGraw-Hill

Name _____

Choose a word in the box to replace the underlined word or words in each sentence.

technique	foolishness	inspire	evaporate
microscope	magnify	negatives	blizzard

1. Lucky for him, Bentley's mother never said, "Stop this <u>silliness</u>! Come in out of the storm at once!" _____

2. Bentley used a <u>scientific instrument that makes small things appear bigger</u> to study snowflakes. _____

3. Bentley's favorite kind of weather was a <u>heavy snowstorm</u>.

   _____

4. Bentley had to develop a special <u>method</u> to photograph snowflakes.

   _____

5. Bentley used the <u>opposites of positives</u> when photographing snowflakes.

   _____

6. Bentley had to work fast to make sure a snowflake didn't <u>dry up</u>. _____

Use each word correctly in a sentence:

7. magnify _____

   _____

8. inspire _____

   _____

> When you **summarize,** you list the important events in a story
> in your own words.

Read the passage and then answer the questions that follow.

Hail is small, round pieces of ice that fall to the ground like a shower of rain. Hail often falls in warm weather, even though it is frozen. There are snowflakes in clouds during thunderstorms. The snowflakes that fall melt in the warm air before they land on the ground. In some thunderstorms, raindrops stick to the snowflakes in the clouds and freeze. The frozen raindrop becomes a small ball of hail. As the small piece of hail begins to fall, air currents push it back up into the clouds. The hail falls through the clouds again. More rain attaches to the hail, and the hail gets bigger. This cycle can happen again and again. At a certain point, the hail is too heavy to be pushed back up. It leaves the cloud and falls to the ground. Hail doesn't melt on its way down. It travels too fast to warm up and turn into rain.

1. How does hail begin to form? _____

_____

2. What happens as hail begins to fall? _____

_____

3. When does the hail drop to the ground? _____

_____

4. Why doesn't hail melt as it falls? _____

At Home: Read or view a local weather report with the student. Have the student summarize what he or she heard.

Name _____

As you read *Snowflake Bentley*, fill in the Main Idea Web.

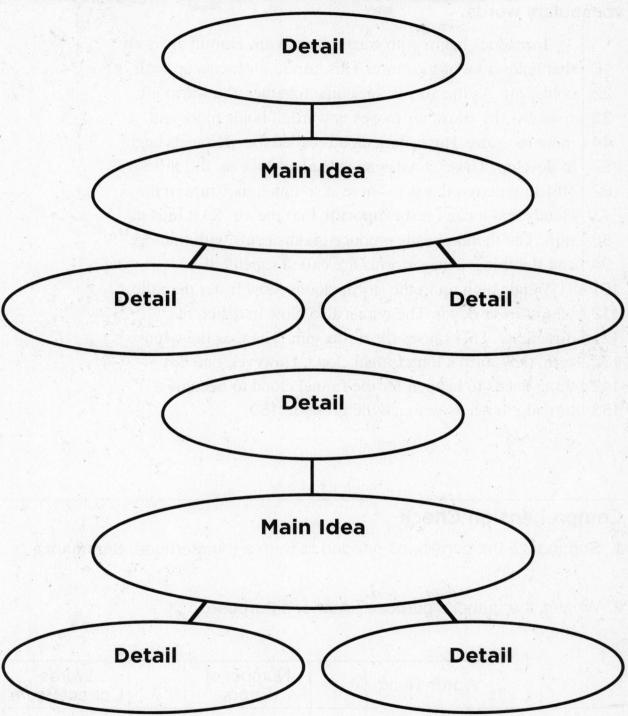

How does the information you wrote in the Main Idea Web help you evaluate *Snowflake Bentley*?

At Home: Have the student use the chart to retell the story.

As I read, I will pay attention to the pronunciation of vocabulary words.

	Tornadoes begin with warm, humid air. Humid air is air
10	that holds a lot of moisture. This humid air meets up with
22	colder air. As the air masses come together, the warm air
33	rises. As the warm air moves upward, it holds more and
44	more moisture. Huge, dark clouds called thunderheads begin
52	to develop. These clouds can spread as wide as 100 miles
62	(161 km) across the sky. There is so much moisture in the
73	clouds that it can't just **evaporate** into the air. So it falls as
86	rain. The thunderheads produce giant storms with thunder
94	and lightning. These storms are called supercells.
101	Winds high up in the storm clouds blow faster than the
112	winds lower down. The winds also blow in different
121	directions. This causes the air to spin. Then, as the winds
132	spin, they form a long funnel cloud. However, one last
142	thing needs to happen for the funnel cloud to become a
153	tornado. It needs to touch the ground. 160

Comprehension Check

1. Summarize the conditions needed to form a thunderhead. **Summarize**

2. What is the author's purpose? **Author's Purpose**

	Words Read	–	Number of Errors	=	Words Correct Score
First Read		–		=	
Second Read		–		=	

At Home: Help the student read the passage, paying attention to the goal at the top of the page.

© Macmillan/McGraw-Hill

> **Imagery** is the use of words to create a picture in the reader's mind.
> **Figurative language** uses words differently from their usual meaning.

Read each haiku and answer the questions that follow.

This light rain falling
Tickles my skin like feathers.
A hot bath calls me.

1. What is light rain compared to? _____

2. Can a hot bath really call someone? What does this mean?

_____

_____

Sun after gray days,
Like Fourth of July fireworks,
Bursts forth bright with joy.

3. What is the sun compared to? _____

4. What figurative language is used in the poem? How can you tell?

_____

_____

A summer hailstorm—
Daisies burrow underground.
They're not meant for ice!

5. What words in this haiku describe something that could not happen?

_____

_____

© Macmillan/McGraw-Hill

At Home: Play a language game with the student. Challenge
each other to describe things using figurative language.

Snowflake Bentley
Grade 4/Unit 3

107

Multiple-meaning words are words that have more than one meaning. You can use the dictionary to find the correct meaning.

pick *verb.* **1.** to select or choose. Pick *a card from the deck.* **2.** to gather with the fingers. *We* picked *blueberries for a pie.* **3.** to pull at and let go; pluck. *She* picked *the strings on the banjo.* *noun.* **1.** a tool with a wooden handle and a metal head, used for breaking rocks and loosening dirt. *He used a* pick *to break the rocks into chunks.* **2.** a thin piece of metal or plastic used for playing a stringed instrument. *I bought a new* pick *at the guitar shop.* **3.** the best of something. *Take your* pick *of the books on the table.*

Use the dictionary entry above to answer the questions.

1. Pick one: playing in the snow or jumping in rain puddles.

   Is *pick* a noun or a verb? _____ Write the definition.

   _____

2. The gold miner's pick was worn down from breaking rocks.

   Is *pick* a noun or a verb? _____ What is the meaning of pick

   in this sentence? _____

3. Did you pick enough blueberries for a pie?

   Is *pick* a noun or a verb? _____ Write the definition.

   _____

4. I strum the guitar with a pick.

   Is *pick* a noun or a verb? _____ Write the definition.

   _____

   _____

At Home: Look for multiple-meaning words in books, magazines, or newspapers. Talk about the different meanings of the words.

A **compound word** is made up of two short words. The two words together make a new word with a new meaning.

When I was at camp this summer, we built a campfire to keep warm at night.

camp + fire = campfire
camp: an outdoor place with tents or cabins.
fire: the flame, heat, and light given off when wood burns.
campfire: an outdoor fire for cooking or keeping warm in a camp.

Draw a line between the two words that make up the compound word. Write the meaning of each word.

1. We had a bad snowstorm.	___ and ___	a. long, thin rope
2. Bentley loved snowflakes.	___ and ___	b. coming into being
3. Hail is made from raindrops.	___ and ___	c. small, thin, flat pieces
4. The child took the towels off the clothesline when the hail came.	___ and ___	d. plants with many long, thin leaves
		e. white crystals of ice
		f. what people wear
5. The child's birthday was in January.	___ and ___	g. windy, unsettled weather
		h. water from clouds
6. The grasshopper hid during the storm.	___ and ___	i. twenty-four hours
		j. small balls of something
		k. someone or something that jumps

© Macmillan/McGraw-Hill

At Home: Challenge the student to think of compound words. You might focus on words about one topic, such as the weather.

Name _____

A. Locate and circle the listed vocabulary words in the puzzle below. Words can be spelled from left to right, right to left, top to bottom, bottom to top, and diagonally.

| loosened | injustice | interfere | segregation | evaporate | awkward |
| sores | ancestors | unfair | avoided | midst | agile |

```
l  b  u  i  w  m  m  i  d  s  t  k  e  z
o  f  i  n  t  e  r  f  e  r  e  a  v  c
o  h  a  j  o  n  r  k  l  o  i  v  s  d
s  t  a  u  n  f  a  i  r  t  y  o  j  r
e  r  g  s  u  q  z  b  m  s  r  i  i  a
n  o  i  t  a  g  e  r  g  e  s  d  e  w
e  u  l  i  p  w  m  c  s  c  a  e  n  k
d  x  e  c  z  n  u  w  s  n  r  d  e  w
t  h  s  e  v  a  p  o  r  a  t  e  n  a
```

B. Write a sentence using each vocabulary word below.

1. tottered _____

2. numerous _____

3. patchwork _____

4. enterprising _____

C. Answer each question using the underlined vocabulary word in your response.

5. What is one kind of <u>foolishness</u> that you learned by experience?

   _____

6. What would your dream <u>venture</u> look like?

   _____

7. What was the most <u>mysterious</u> civilization you have heard about?

   _____

8. What can happen when you <u>magnify</u> a problem?

   _____

D. Choose the vocabulary word that correctly completes the sentence and write it on the line. Then make up a sentence that includes that word.

9. **technique   responsibility**   We all have a _____ to be good citizens.

   _____

10. **proclaimed   identified**   It was _____ throughout the kingdom that the prince planned to marry.

    _____

11. **mysterious   unsuspecting**   The hunters waited in the tall grass for

    the _____ ducks.

    _____

12. Write a sentence using the word *guardian*.

    _____

Use the words in the box to complete the sentences below.

risks	desperate	obedience	appreciated
bluffing	neglected	endured	misunderstood

1. My dog has often taken _____ to save me from danger.

2. Once I _____ to look both ways before crossing the street, and I almost walked into a bus.

3. I really _____ that my clever dog barked and jumped up on me. He probably saved my life!

4. The only time I scold Sparky is when he tries to eat food from our

   table. Each time he looks at me as if he has _____ great suffering.

5. Once I sent him to _____ school.

6. Sparky pretended to learn all the commands, but he was only

   _____.

Write two sentences, each using one of the vocabulary words.

7. _____

   _____

8. _____

   _____

Sometimes when you read a story, you have to **draw a conclusion** about a character or an aspect of the plot. To draw a conclusion, use what the author tells you and what you know from your own experience to make a statement about what's happening in the story.

Read the story. Then draw conclusions to answer the questions.

Fred and Roberto lived next door to each other. Whenever Roberto looked out the window and saw that Fred's owner was taking him for a walk, Roberto would scratch at the front door and whine until Mrs. Marsh got his leash and took him out.

One day Fred came bounding into Roberto's backyard. "I'm running away," he told Roberto. "Mr. Gomez doesn't appreciate the way I bring him his slippers when he comes home from work."

"Don't do it," he advised Fred. "Give Mr. Gomez a little more time to get to know you. He will appreciate you when he gets to know you better."

"You may be right," Fred agreed. "I'll give him another chance."

1. How do you know that this story cannot be true?

_____

2. How do you know that Fred has not been with Mr. Gomez for very long?

_____

3. How do you know that Mrs. Marsh was good to Roberto?

_____

4. How do you know that Fred doesn't really want to run away?

_____

© Macmillan/McGraw-Hill

At Home: Have the student read a story or article and draw conclusions about the characters.

Dear Mrs. LaRue
Grade 4/Unit 4
113

Name _____

As you read *Dear Mrs. LaRue,* fill in the Conclusions Chart.

Text Clues	Conclusions

How does completing the Conclusions Chart help you to generate
questions about *Dear Mrs. LaRue*?

At Home: Have the student use the chart to retell the story.

© Macmillan/McGraw-Hill

As I read, I will pay attention to punctuation.

	Presidents have kept a wide range of pets. These
9	animals have included cows, mice, goats, and birds. But
18	dogs have been the most popular presidential pets.
26	Dogs are loyal and loving. They make their owners
35	feel **appreciated**. Like other dog owners, many Presidents
43	have enjoyed the special friendship that dogs can give.
52	Many people believe that dogs help Presidents gain
60	support from Americans. Pictures of Presidents playing
67	with their dogs can make the Presidents seem likable and
77	help them win votes.
81	More than 200 dogs of various breeds have lived at the
91	White House. Some of these White House dogs served
100	as guard dogs. Others played with the Presidents' children.
109	And others clearly belonged to the Presidents and were
118	their personal four-legged friends. A few presidential
125	pooches were even as well known as their masters. Let's
135	take a look at some of the famous "First Dogs" of America. 147

Comprehension Check

1. Why might people prefer a president who has a dog as a pet? **Draw Conclusions**

2. Why did the author write this passage about presidential dogs? **Author's Purpose**

	Words Read	–	Number of Errors	=	Words Correct Score
First Read		–		=	
Second Read		–		=	

At Home: Help the student read the passage, paying attention to the goal at the top of the page.

Dear Mrs. LaRue
Grade 4/Unit 4

115

Name _____

A **line graph** is a good way to show how something changes over time. Points on the graph are connected by lines that make it easy to tell whether the occurrences of something increased or decreased as time passed.

Look at the line graph below and answer the questions.

Number of Search Dog Requests in Vail, Colorado

1. During which two months were the largest number of search dogs

   needed? _____

2. How many search dogs were needed in May? _____

3. In which month were 5 search dogs needed? _____

4. Which two months had the same number of searches?

   _____

5. How many more searches were requested in January than in July?

   _____

At Home: Have the student make a line graph of the number of certain things in a week. For example, he or she might graph the number of letters that arrive each day.

© Macmillan/McGraw-Hill

When you put the prefix **mis-** in front of a word, it changes the meaning of the word. **Mis-** means "badly" or "incorrectly."

Add the prefix mis- to each word. Then write a sentence with the new word.

New Word

1. judge _____

2. spell _____

3. treat _____

4. read _____

5. behave _____

Sentence

1. _____

_____

2. _____

_____

3. _____

_____

4. _____

_____

5. _____

_____

At Home: Have the student identify and define two other words that include the prefix mis-.

Dear Mrs. LaRue
Grade 4/Unit 4   117

When you add **-ed** or **-ing** to a word, sometimes you have to add or drop a letter before adding the ending.
- If the word has a short vowel sound and ends in a single consonant, double the last letter before adding the ending.
- If the word ends in **e**, drop the **e** before adding the ending.

Complete the table by writing the correct -ed and -ing forms of each of these words.

Base Word	Word + *ing*	Word + *ed*
1. hop	_____	_____
2. hope	_____	_____
3. flip	_____	_____
4. force	_____	_____
5. tap	_____	_____
6. tape	_____	_____

Write four sentences, each using one of the words above.

7. _____

8. _____

9. _____

10. _____

© Macmillan/McGraw-Hill

At Home: Play a verb game. Say one-syllable verbs and have the student add -ed or -ing to them, spelling the completed words.

| fade | cautiously | crisscrossed | wisdom |
| jealousy | disguised | faint | |

Answer each question by using a vocabulary word that means the same as the underlined phrase.

1. Does light <u>grow dim</u> after the sun sets?

_____

2. Is it hard to hear a very <u>slight, soft</u> whisper?

_____

3. Do older people have more <u>good sense</u> than younger people?

_____

4. Was the snowy parking lot <u>marked by crossed lines</u> with tire tracks?

_____

5. Did the student enter the principal's office <u>hesitantly</u>?

_____

6. At the costume party, who came <u>dressed up</u> as someone famous?

_____

7. Do silver-medal winners look at the gold medal with <u>envy</u>?

_____

8. Now write your own question and answer following the model.

Question: _____

Answer: _____

Name _____

Sometimes when you read, you have to **draw conclusions** about something in the story. To draw a conclusion, use what the author tells you and what you know from your own experience.

Read the story below. Then answer the questions that follow.

"Look at my new invention," Matthew said to his friend Abby. "It's a math homework machine. I invented a robot that will do math problems."

"How does it work?" Abby asked. She and Matthew were sitting side by side on the front porch of Matthew's house, after school. Abby was interested in Matthew's machine because they both had a lot of homework.

"You put the math page in here," Matthew said, "and the answers come out there." He put in a page of math problems to show Abby how the machine was supposed to work, but when the answer page came out, this short message was printed on it: "You need to do this work yourself, or you will never be as smart as I am. Your friend, Ricky Robot."

1. How do you know that Matthew did not like to do math homework? _____

_____

2. What can you conclude about the robot that Matthew invented?

_____

_____

3. How do you know that Abby and Matthew's teachers believed that

homework was a good idea? _____

_____

4. How do you know this story is not true? _____

_____

At Home: Have the student choose a favorite character from TV or the movies and draw conclusions about that character based on his or her actions.

Name _____

As you read *The Blind Hunter,* fill in the Conclusions Chart.

Text Clues	Conclusions

How does completing the Conclusions Chart help you to generate
questions about *The Blind Hunter*?

 At Home: Have the student use the chart to retell the story.

As I read, I will pay attention to pauses and stops in each sentence.

	You may know people who like to talk about
9	themselves. Marie Curie was not that kind of person. She
19	went about her work quietly and **cautiously**. She didn't
28	brag about what she did, although she could have. She was
39	a woman of great **wisdom**. Marie Curie made discoveries
48	that changed the world.
52	Marie Curie's work opened up a new field of medicine
62	called radiology. Her experiments led to better ways of
71	treating people with cancer and other diseases.
78	She was the first woman ever to win a Nobel Prize.
89	This is a special prize given each year to people who do
101	important work. Years later, Marie won a second Nobel
110	Prize. She was the first person ever to do so.
120	Marie Curie lived at a time when few women were able
131	to be scientists. She was born poor and was often ill. Yet
143	she rose above all that to become a hero to the world. 155

Comprehension Check

1. How do you know that Marie Curie was taken seriously by the science community? **Draw Conclusions**

2. Summarize the description of Marie Curie. **Summarize**

	Words Read	–	Number of Errors	=	Words Correct Score
First Read		–		=	
Second Read		–		=	

© Macmillan/McGraw-Hill

At Home: Help the student read the passage, paying attention to the goal at the top of the page.

A **glossary** is like a small dictionary found at the back of a book. It lists important or difficult words found in the book in alphabetical order. The glossary gives the meanings and pronunciations of the words.

Use the glossary below to answer the questions.

landscape 1. The stretch of land that can be seen from a place; view. The train passengers watched the passing *landscape*. 2. A picture of such a view. The artist painted a *landscape*. *Noun* To make an area of land more beautiful by planting trees, shrubs, and by designing gardens. A gardener will *landscape* the grounds. *Verb* **land•scape** (land´ skāp´), *noun, plural* **landscapes;** verb **landscaped, landscaping**

laser A device that makes a narrow but strong beam of light. A laser may be used to perform surgery, cut metal, or send messages. **la•ser** (lā´zər) *noun, plural* **lasers.**

1. How are the glossary words arranged?

_____

2. As what parts of speech may *landscape* be used?

_____

3. How might a laser be used?

_____

4. Why wasn't the word *lantern* in the glossary?

_____

At Home: Have the student write a sentence with each glossary word.

> **Word families** are groups of words that all share a word **root**
> or other **part**. You can use what you know about one word to
> find out the meanings of other members of its family.
> For example, the word **wisdom** belongs to a family of words
> that includes **kingdom** and **freedom**.

The syllable *wis* is related to "wise." One meaning of the suffix
-dom is "state or condition of being a certain way." Based on
this meaning of *-dom*, write a definition of *wisdom*.

1. _____

The syllable *-dom* can also mean "land ruled by." Classify
kingdom, freedom, and *dukedom* according to which meaning of
-dom they have.

Land Ruled By

2. _____

3. _____

State or Condition of Being

4. _____

Fit the above words into these sentences.

5. She was the loveliest lady in the _____.

6. We have the _____ to vote in this country.

© Macmillan/McGraw-Hill

At Home: Have the student use the words *freedom, wisdom,*
and *kingdom* in sentences of their own.

When words end in a consonant + **y**, you do two things to add endings like **-er** or **-ed**. First you change the **y** to **i**. Then you add the ending.

Change *y* to *i* and add the indicated ending to each word. Then write the new word in the blank.

lazy + er   1. _____

reply + ed   2. _____

worry + es   3. _____

happy + est   4. _____

empty + er   5. _____

family + es   6. _____

dizzy + est   7. _____

funny + er   8. _____

Follow the model and write four more words.

9. _____   _____

10. _____   _____

11. _____   _____

12. _____   _____

At Home: Have the student find words in a magazine or newspaper article that end with a consonant + *y*. Have him or her add the endings *-es*, *-er*, and *-est*.

The Blind Hunter
Grade 4/Unit 4   125

Name _____

Complete each sentence with a word from the box.

| electrical | globe | fuels | decayed |

1. The new _____ cars will help use less gasoline.

2. A horrible smell comes from the remains of animals that have

   _____.

3. Scientists are always trying to produce better _____ and make them burn cleaner.

4. Countries from around the _____ will participate in the conference.

Now write a paragraph in which you use each vocabulary word at least once.

_____

_____

_____

_____

_____

_____

_____

> **Persuasion** is convincing other people to agree with your ideas or opinions. Writers can use reasons, facts, examples, or feelings to try to persuade people.

Read the selection below. Then answer the questions that follow.

No matter where you live, it is a good idea to walk rather than use a car. Walking is good for you! The exercise helps to keep you healthy. My dad stopped driving last year and now he's running in races!

Walking also cuts down on automobile use. This helps reduce pollution and is a good way to make our town safer. If fewer people are driving, there will be fewer automobile accidents.

1. What is the writer trying to persuade you to do?

_____

2. What is one of the reasons the writer gives for his or her point of view?

_____

_____

3. Write an additional reason that supports the writer's point of view.

_____

4. What example does the writer give to support the statement that walking

is good for you? _____

_____

5. Has the writer persuaded you to walk instead of ride? Why or why not?

_____

At Home: Talk about the different ways that television tries to persuade you in your daily life.

The Power of Oil
Grade 4/Unit 4   127

As you read *The Power of Oil*, fill in the Inference/Opinion Web.

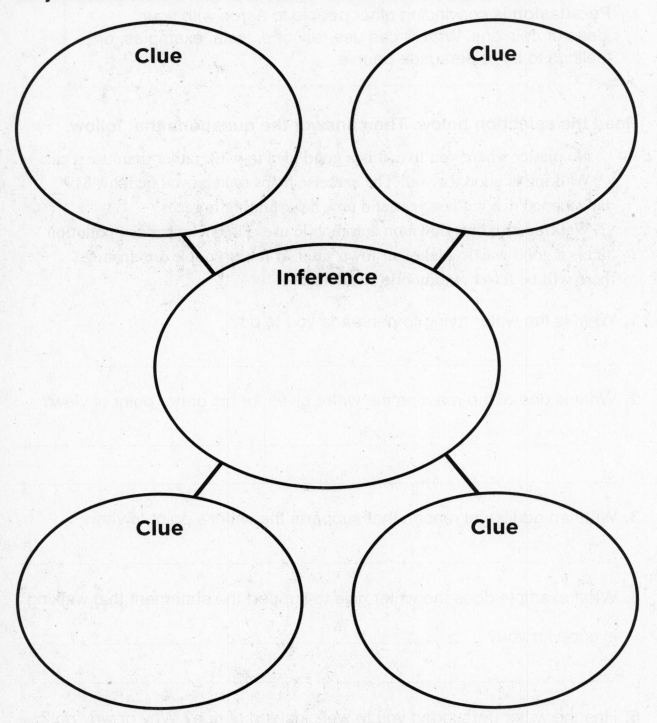

Clue

Clue

Inference

Clue

Clue

© Macmillan/McGraw-Hill

How does the information you wrote in the Inference/Opinion Web
help you generate questions about *The Power of Oil*?

At Home: Have the student use the chart to retell the story.

As I read, I will pay attention to my pronunciation of vocabulary words and other difficult words.

	The Hoover Dam brought the Colorado River under
8	control. The dam also created a reserve of water. The water
19	was used to irrigate dry farmland. It was also used as a
31	water supply by nearby cities and towns.
38	But the biggest benefit of Hoover Dam is its
47	hydroelectric power. The Hoover Dam makes a huge
55	amount of electricity. Every year it brings power to
64	1.3 million people in California, Nevada, and Arizona.
71	As an energy source, the Hoover Dam is clean and
81	cheap to run. It does not pollute the air the way fossil **fuels**
94	would. However, this huge dam has had some bad effects
104	on the environment. The landscape of the area will never
114	be the same. The river can no longer carry rich soil to the
127	lands it flooded. Fish and other wildlife have lost their homes.
138	But the Hoover Dam is here to stay. It is a modern
150	wonder of the United States. 155

Comprehension Check

1. How does the author persuade the reader that the Hoover Dam is helpful? **Persuasion**

2. Compare the effects of fossil fuels with the effects of the dam. **Compare and Contrast**

	Words Read	–	Number of Errors	=	Words Correct Score
First Read		–		=	
Second Read		–		=	

© Macmillan/McGraw-Hill

At Home: Help the student read the passage, paying attention to the goal at the top of the page.

The Power of Oil
Grade 4/Unit 4

129

Name _____

You can use a **search engine** to find information on the
Internet. Type one or more **keywords** that describe your topic
into the search engine. Then click *Search.* The search results
will bring up a list of Web pages that have the keywords you
entered. Click a page name to see it on your computer.

**Look at the page of search results below. Then answer the
questions that follow.**

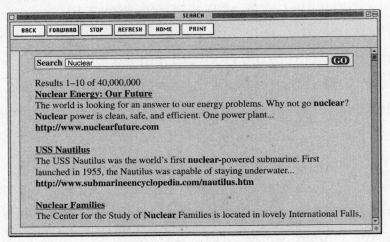

1. How many total results did the search return? _____

2. What was the search keyword? _____

3. What's another keyword you could use to bring up more information

   about nuclear energy? _____

4. What would happen if you clicked on the USS *Nautilus* link?

   _____

5. Where on the page would you enter more keywords for another search?

   _____

At Home: Pick a topic with the student. Ask what keywords
he or she would use to look up the topic on the Internet.

© Macmillan/McGraw-Hill

When you're reading, you may find words that you do not know. When this happens, look in the text for **context clues**. You may find words and phrases that give you the **definition** of an unfamiliar word.

Read each sentence. Define each underlined word. Write your definition on the line and circle the context clues that helped you determine the word's meaning.

1. We spun the <u>globe</u> of the world, looking for the countries of Africa.

   _____

2. You need electricity to run TVs, refrigerators, and other <u>electrical</u> appliances.

   _____

3. Do your parents use several <u>fuels</u> to create energy to heat your home?

   _____

4. Since the animals' remains had <u>decayed</u>, they had broken down to the point that we couldn't tell what they were.

   _____

Now answer the following questions about each word.

5. What shape is a <u>globe</u>? _____

6. Name two <u>fuels</u>. _____

   _____

© Macmillan/McGraw-Hill

At Home: Read a newspaper article with the student. When you come to an unfamiliar word, have the student look for context clues to determine the word's meaning.

The Power of Oil
Grade 4/Unit 4

131

- Words like *spool*, *grew*, *move*, *soup*, and *suit* have the **/ü/** sound.
- Words like *brooks* and *should* have the **/ů/** sound.
- Words like *cubes* and *mule* have the **/ū/** sound.

Notice that *oo* and *ou* can stand for different sounds.
Remember which sound they stand for in each word you learn.

Read the words in the box. Then put each word under the correct heading.

would	knew	books	food
dune	looking	wood	prove
you'll	scoop	used	cute

/ü/	/ů/	/ū/
_____	_____	_____
_____	_____	_____
_____	_____	_____
_____	_____	_____
_____	_____	_____

At Home: Have the student identify as many spellings as he or she can for the /ü/ and /ů/ sounds.

dove	snoring	tangles	unique
politicians	massive	rumbling	

Fill in each blank with the correct vocabulary word from the list at the top of the page.

1. The _____ boulder weighed over ten tons.

2. After a day at the ocean, the girl's long hair became a mess of

   _____.

3. Candidates who run in elections are called _____.

4. To make sure that her quilt would be _____, Grandma used an unusual pattern for organizing her patches.

5. The hawk _____ quickly to catch the rabbit.

6. My grandfather's loud _____ eventually woke him up.

7. The _____ of the thunder scared my dog.

Choose three vocabulary words and use them in one sentence.

8. _____

_____

_____

_____

_____

The **sequence of events** in a story is the order in which things happen. Keeping track of the sequence of events helps you make sense of what is happening in a story.

Read the story below. Then number the events that follow to show the correct sequence.

Miranda's parents were planning a trip to Mexico to go whale watching. Miranda's mother bought airline tickets on a travel Web site. Miranda's father asked his boss for time off. Miranda asked a neighbor to feed the family pets. Miranda's mother asked the post office to hold their mail.

On the day of the trip, the family drove to the airport. They stood in line and went through security. Finally they boarded the airplane and took off for Mexico.

1. Miranda's mother asked the post office to hold the mail. _____

2. They stood in line and went through security. _____

3. The family boarded the plane and took off for Mexico. _____

4. Miranda's parents were planning a trip to Mexico. _____

5. Miranda's father asked his boss for time off. _____

6. Miranda's mother bought airline tickets on a travel Web site. _____

7. Miranda asked a neighbor to feed the family pets. _____

8. On the day of the trip, the family drove to the airport. _____

At Home: Together with the student, recall the events of a family trip in random order. Then have him or her number the events in the correct sequence on a sheet of paper.

© Macmillan/McGraw-Hill

Name _____

As you read *Adelina's Whales*, fill in the Sequence Chart.

```
┌─────────────────────────────────────┐
│                                      │
│                                      │
│                                      │
│                                      │
└─────────────────────────────────────┘
                    │
                    ▼
┌─────────────────────────────────────┐
│                                      │
│                                      │
│                                      │
│                                      │
└─────────────────────────────────────┘
                    │
                    ▼
┌─────────────────────────────────────┐
│                                      │
│                                      │
│                                      │
│                                      │
└─────────────────────────────────────┘
```

How does the information you wrote in the Sequence Chart help you
to analyze the text structure of *Adelina's Whales*?

© Macmillan/McGraw-Hill

At Home: Have the student use the chart to retell the story.

Name _____

As I read, I will pay attention to tempo and match the action in the story.

	Did you know that whales talk to each other? Whales
10	make sounds for different reasons. Some sounds are used to
20	locate calves. Others are used to find mates. Whales even use
31	sounds to warn other pod members that a predator is around.
42	Toothed whales click and whistle in order to locate food.
52	Baleen whales make knocking, moaning, **snoring**, and
59	**rumbling** noises. Humpback whales sing, but not during
67	feeding season. They save their tunes for the warmer waters
77	where they spend their breeding season. Some scientists
85	believe they are singing love songs. Other scientists think
94	they are sending out threats, like "Go away!" We may never
105	know exactly why whales sing.
110	Some humpback whales swim up to the surface and take
120	a few breaths. Then they dive under the water and start to
132	sing. They do not move when they sing. Their underwater
142	songs can be heard for miles. Sometimes they sing for a half
154	hour without stopping. 157

Comprehension Check

1. What actions does a humpback whale take when it sings? **Sequence**

2. Why might a whale need to communicate with another whale? **Draw Conclusions**

	Words Read	–	Number of Errors	=	Words Correct Score
First Read		–		=	
Second Read		–		=	

At Home: Help the student read the passage, paying attention to the goal at the top of the page.

The **rhyme scheme** of a poem is the pattern of rhymes at the end of each line. The poem's **meter** is the way that accented and unaccented syllables are arranged in the poem. You can think of it as the poem's rhythm.

1. **Read the following limerick by Edward Lear. Circle the rhyming words at the end of each line. Then put an *a* next to the first set of rhyming words and a *b* next to the second set of rhyming words to identify the poem's rhyme scheme.**

There was an Old Man with a beard, _____

Who said "It is just as I feared!— _____

Two Owls and a Hen, _____

Four Larks and a Wren, _____

Have all built their nests in my beard!" _____

2. **Read the first line of the poem. How would you describe the meter of this line?**

_____

3. **Now write your own limerick below.**

_____

_____

_____

_____

_____

At Home: Have the student explain the rhyme scheme and
meter for the limerick above.

Adelina's Whales
Grade 4/Unit 4

137

Homographs are words that have the same spelling but different meanings. They may also have different pronunciations.

Read the list of homographs and their meanings. Then read the sentences and decide the meaning of the underlined homograph. Write the letter of the correct meaning in the blank next to the sentence.

dove – a. past tense of dive   **b.** a kind of bird

fluke – c. part of a whale's tail   **d.** something lucky

1. The whale splashed the surface of the water with its <u>fluke</u>. _____

2. The eagle <u>dove</u> for its prey. _____

3. It was a <u>fluke</u> that my mother won the game. _____

4. The bird watchers saw a mourning <u>dove</u> sitting in a tree. _____

Pick another homograph. Write one sentence for each meaning of the word.

5. _____

_____

6. _____

_____

At Home: Together with the student, think of another homograph pair. Are the pronunciations different or the same?

The /oi/ sound can be spelled with **oi** as in **foil** or with **oy** as in **boy**. The /ou/ sound can be spelled with **ou** as in **couch** or with **ow** as in **now**. Keep in mind, though, that not all words containing **oi** have the /oi/ sound and not all words spelled with **ou** and **ow** have the /ou/ sound.

In each row of words below, there is one word that does not belong. If the word does not have the same sound as the others, make an X over it. If the word is a homograph, sometimes pronounced like the other words and sometimes pronounced differently, put an asterisk (*) next to it. Then on the blank line, add another word that belongs with the group you made.

1. joy	foil	employ	onion	_____
2. bow	allowed	south	outside	_____
3. coil	destroy	oil	going	_____
4. mouth	doubt	through	how	_____
5. broil	doing	spoil	noise	_____
6. sow	tower	frown	sprout	_____
7. couch	dough	cloud	crowd	_____
8. enjoy	soil	shooing	toys	_____
9. now	enough	crown	proud	_____
10. brow	cow	low	down	_____
11. annoy	voices	boil	porpoise	_____
12. thought	shower	loud	trout	_____

© Macmillan/McGraw-Hill

At Home: Have the student write a silly poem using some of the *oi* and *ou* words from the above list.

Adelina's Whales
Grade 4/Unit 4

139

Name _____

| coral | brittle | current | suburbs |
| reef | eventually | partnership | |

Complete each sentence with a word from the box.

1. On our vacation we went snorkeling and saw pink _____.

2. The blizzard closed the airport for several hours, but planes

   _____ were able to take off.

3. My father took the train from our station in the _____ into
   the city each morning.

4. During the storm the wind snapped the _____ tree branch.

5. The hidden _____ ripped into the bottom of the boat.

6. The fast-moving _____ of the river swept the dead tree
   out to sea.

7. My friends and I set up a business _____.

**Choose five of the vocabulary words and use them in
three sentences.**

8. _____

   _____

9. _____

   _____

10. _____

   _____

When you **compare** two things, you look at ways in which they are alike. When you **contrast** them, you focus on how they are different.

**Read the passage about sharks and dolphins below.
Then answer the questions that follow.**

Dolphins and sharks both live in the ocean, but they are different in many ways. Dolphins are not fish, but warm-blooded mammals. Dolphins have lungs and come up to the surface to breathe.

Sharks are fish, with gills instead of lungs. Some sharks live deep in the ocean, while others live near the surface.

Sharks and dolphins are alike in some ways, too. Both eat fish, and some kinds live together in rivers and lakes in Central and South America.

Compare sharks and dolphins and list two ways that they are alike.

1. _____

   _____

2. _____

   _____

Contrast sharks and dolphins and list two ways in which they are different.

3. _____

   _____

4. _____

   _____

© Macmillan/McGraw-Hill

At Home: Ask the student to compare and contrast two other animals.

At Home in the Coral Reef
Grade 4/Unit 4

141

Name _____

As you read *At Home in the Coral Reef*, fill in the Venn Diagram.

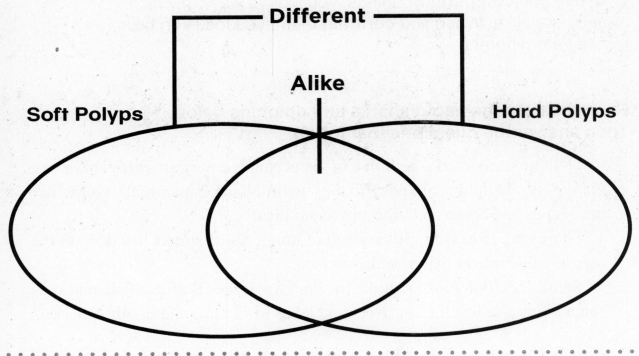

Different

Alike

Soft Polyps   **Hard Polyps**

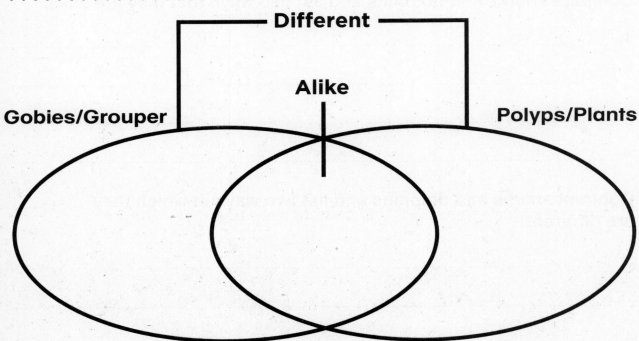

Different

Alike

Gobies/Grouper   **Polyps/Plants**

How does completing the Venn Diagram help you to analyze the text structure of *At Home in the Coral Reef*?

© Macmillan/McGraw-Hill

At Home: Have the student use the chart to retell the story.

Name _____

As I read, I will pay attention to my pronunciation of vocabulary words.

	Life in a tide pool is difficult. The **temperature** may
10	range from very hot in the daytime to very cold at night.
22	Twice a day, during high tide, ocean waves rush in and fill
34	the tide pool with water. At low tide the water goes out
46	again. The same tide pool may be completely dry.
55	Tide pool animals must hang on tight at high tide and
66	keep themselves wet at low tide. They must adapt to
76	both heat and cold. And they must defend themselves
85	against becoming another creature's lunch. Only the most
93	adaptable tide pool animals can survive.
99	The barnacle is an example of a true tide pool survivor.
110	A barnacle is born swimming freely. But soon after that,
120	it finds a rock or other hard surface in a tide pool. The
133	animal cements itself there for life. 139

Comprehension Check

1. How is a tide pool different from a part of the ocean that is always under water? **Compare and Contrast**

2. Why does the barnacle need to cement itself to a rock? **Draw Conclusions**

	Words Read	–	Number of Errors	=	Words Correct Score
First Read		–		=	
Second Read		–		=	

At Home: Help the student read the passage, paying attention to the goal at the top of the page.

Name _____

> The main character in a story is called the **protagonist.**
> **Hyperbole** is the use of exaggeration to make a point or create
> a sense of drama.

Read the passage below. Then answer the questions that follow.

Devin was amazed by what he saw when he jumped into the water.
Through his mask, he could see different kinds of fish flitting around the
coral. "There must be a million of them," he thought to himself. Some
shimmered so brightly that they must have been made of silver. Others
were bright blue, red, and yellow. It was as if a museum full of paintings
had been turned into fish and let loose among the coral.

To his left he could see his sister Brianna swimming near a big fan-
shaped piece of coral. He motioned toward the surface, and they both
swam up and stuck their heads out.

"Is this great or what?" Devin asked.

"Yeah!" said Brianna. "I'm going to spend my whole vacation out here."

1. Who is the story's protagonist? _____

What are two examples of hyperbole from the story?

2. _____

_____

3. _____

_____

Use hyperbole to create your own description of a coral reef.

4. _____

_____

At Home: Together with the student, take turns using
hyperbole to describe things in your home.

© Macmillan/McGraw-Hill

> **Context clues** can help readers determine the meaning of an unfamiliar word. Sometimes writers will provide context clues through a **description** that makes the meaning of a word clearer.
>
> Example: *My uncle could never eat clams or oysters because he was allergic to **mollusks**.* You can use the context clues *clams* and *oysters* to figure out the meaning of the word **mollusks**.

Underline the context clues that describe the word in dark type. Then write the word's definition.

1. I saw all kinds of **marine** life swimming underwater at the aquarium.

   Definition: _____

2. After the earthquake, there were a few smaller **tremors** that shook the ground.

   Definition: _____

3. Some fish feed on **plankton** because these tiny plants and animals are very nutritious.

   Definition: _____

4. To put out the fire, the man **doused** the flames with a bucket of water.

   Definition: _____

5. The captain pulled the **rudder** hard to the left to steer the ship away from the rocks.

   Definition: _____

6. The **brilliant** sunshine streamed in through the window and lit up the room.

   Definition: _____

© Macmillan/McGraw-Hill

At Home: Choose two other words. Then ask the student to write a sentence that includes descriptive context clues for each one.

At Home in the Coral Reef
Grade 4/Unit 4   145

The underlined letters in the following words show you different ways to spell the /ô/ sound: **ba<u>l</u>d, st<u>al</u>k, str<u>aw</u>, c<u>au</u>ght.** Notice that in **bald** you pronounce the **l,** but that in **stalk** you do not.

Read the list of words below. Then sort the words into two columns. The left column is for words with the /ô/ sound. The right column is for other words.

laws	catch	malt	bows
sale	wall	band	talking
wail	mall	strawberry	taught

Words with /ô/

_____

_____

_____

_____

_____

_____

_____

Other Words

_____

_____

_____

_____

_____

_____

_____

© Macmillan/McGraw-Hill

At Home: Ask the student to identify four other words with the /ô/ sound.

A. Find and circle the vocabulary words in the puzzle.
Words can be spelled left to right, right to left, top to bottom,
bottom to top, and diagonally.

crisscrossed   endured   electrical   unique   snoring   politicians

```
w  f  u  c  c  p  i  j  w  m  n  e
r  t  s  n  r  b  x  t  i  j  g  s
p  p  o  l  i  t  i  c  i  a  n  s
o  a  w  n  s  q  b  a  j  c  i  l
r  l  r  x  s  t  u  h  k  e  r  f
u  j  u  e  c  r  s  e  n  r  o  m
s  d  f  n  r  u  d  a  q  u  n  k
l  r  h  z  o  m  o  w  d  b  s  x
g  w  e  l  s  t  k  v  s  u  x  g
m  s  q  u  s  t  w  t  v  i  l  t
a  y  e  l  e  c  t  r  i  c  a  l
d  e  r  u  d  n  e  j  r  p  w  o
```

B. Complete each sentence with a vocabulary word from
Exercise A.

1. The sound of my dog _____ loudly in his sleep woke
me up.

2. How many _____ appliances are there in your home?

3. Ralph's dog _____ training classes just to get the treats.

4. What makes humpback whales _____ among all whales?

5. Our class wrote to _____ to ask them to pass laws that
would protect sea life.

Name _____

C. Draw a line to match the definition to the vocabulary word.

6. not properly cared for

a. massive

7. pretending or fooling, usually by
acting bigger or more powerful

b. disguised

c. desperate

8. willing to do anything to
get what you want

d. neglected

9. very large

e. bluffing

10. changed the appearance of in order to hide

D. Write the vocabulary word that means almost the same thing as the underlined word.

| eventually | globe | tangles | brittle | cautiously |

11. I had to be very careful handling the <u>breakable</u> coral.

_____

12. Sam <u>finally</u> collected a new quarter from each of the fifty states.

_____

13. After our walk in the woods, I had to comb the <u>knots</u> out of my dog's fur.

_____

14. Maria <u>carefully</u> crossed the street. _____

15. How many times did that satellite circle the <u>Earth</u>? _____

| snuffled | selecting | positive | consisted | peculiar | advanced |

Complete each sentence with a word from the box.

1. The dog _____ loudly as he sniffed for more food in his dish.

2. Ted had trouble _____ a different book because he liked to read only mysteries.

3. "You have a _____ taste in music," Tobie told Andre. "I never thought I would meet a nine-year-old who liked Bach."

4. Andre's choices at the library always _____ of history books about the period too.

5. "I am absolutely _____ that you will love this book about horses," Laura assured Marie.

6. Both girls then argued over which of the two was the more _____ reader.

Write a sentence using the word listed.

7. peculiar _____

_____

8. selecting _____

_____

Write a definition of the listed word, using your own words.

9. snuffled _____

10. advanced _____

A **summary** is a short retelling of a story. To **summarize** what you have read, include only the most important information.

Read the passage below. Then answer the questions that follow.

I love the public library in my town. It's in an old building. I can find everything I need there. The books are organized by subject and author. That makes it easy to find what I need. Then I can take my books home.

Libraries have only a few rules. You must have a library card to take out a book. There is no charge for checking out a book, but many libraries ask that books be returned after three weeks. If you don't return books on time, you must pay a fine. Some libraries limit the number of books you can check out at once.

Most libraries today have computers. If you have to write a report for a homework assignment, the computer can help you find the information you need to know.

1. What should you include in a summary?

_____

2. If you were summarizing the passage above, would you include the information that you must have a library card to check out a book? Why?

_____

3. If you were summarizing the passage above, would you include the information that the library is in an old building? Why?

_____

4. Now write a summary of the passage above in your own words.

_____

_____

_____

_____

© Macmillan/McGraw-Hill

At Home: Together with the student, take turns giving summaries of your day. Make sure your summaries include only the most important information rather than every detail.

Name _____

**As you read *Because of Winn-Dixie*, fill in the
Summarizing Chart.**

```
┌─────────────────────────────────────────────┐
│                                             │
│                                             │
│                                             │
└─────────────────────────────────────────────┘
                     │
                     ▼
┌─────────────────────────────────────────────┐
│                                             │
│                                             │
│                                             │
└─────────────────────────────────────────────┘
                     │
                     ▼
┌─────────────────────────────────────────────┐
│                                             │
│                                             │
│                                             │
└─────────────────────────────────────────────┘
                     │
                     ▼
┌─────────────────────────────────────────────┐
│                                             │
│                                             │
│                                             │
└─────────────────────────────────────────────┘
                     │
                     ▼
┌─────────────────────────────────────────────┐
│                                             │
│                                             │
│                                             │
└─────────────────────────────────────────────┘
```

**How does the information you wrote in the Summarizing Chart help
you to evaluate *Because of Winn-Dixie*?**

At Home: Have the student use the chart to retell the story.

As I read, I will pay attention to end punctuation.

	Nate Jasper fumbled for his library card and handed it
10	to Ms. Kim, the librarian. He was checking out books
20	about life in the American colonies for a social studies
30	report. He hadn't realized it was his turn because he
40	was distracted by a sign taped to the wall beside the
51	circulation desk.
53	The sign read: "First Annual Highland Drawing
60	Contest. Prizes to be awarded for drawings that best show
70	the exciting and unique beauty of Highland, Vermont."
78	"I see that our drawing contest has caught your eye,"
88	said Ms. Kim. "Are you an artist?"
95	"Yeah, I guess I am," said Nate. "But I've never entered
106	a contest."
108	"Well, why not consider making this your first?" asked
117	Ms. Kim. "We have a Young Artists division, and we need
128	people like you to help make the contest a success. The
139	winning drawings will be displayed here in the Highland
148	Public Library. Here, take a flyer and think about it." 158

Comprehension Check

1. What does Ms. Kim say to Nate? **Summarize**

2. Why is Nate a good candidate to enter the contest? **Draw Conclusions**

	Words Read	–	Number of Errors	=	Words Correct Score
First Read		–		=	
Second Read		–		=	

© Macmillan/McGraw-Hill

At Home: Help the student read the passage, paying attention to the goal at the top of the page.

> **Onomatopoeia** is the use of a word to imitate a sound.
> A **simile** compares two different things using *like* or *as*.

Read the poem below. Then answer the questions that follow.

Books

What can you do with books, anyway?
You can laugh at them,
   frown at them, slam them shut.
You can stack them cover to cover
   till they're as tall as a skyscraper.
You can stuff them in your backpack
   till it's heavy like an elephant.
Or you can take one, crack it open,
   and read.

1. Which word in the third line of the poem is an example of onomatopoeia?

_____

2. Write the two similes that appear in the poem.

_____

_____

3. What two things are being compared in the similes you wrote above?

_____

_____

4. Why is the poet's use of the word *slam* an example of onomatopoeia?

_____

_____

At Home: Together with the student, take turns using similes to compare items in your home.

Because of Winn-Dixie
Grade 4/Unit 5

153

Practice

Vocabulary Strategy:
Connotation/
Denotation

Name _____

> The dictionary definition of a word is its **denotation**.
> The feelings associated with a word are its **connotation**.

The bold words in each pair of sentences below have similar denotations, but their connotations are different. Write the feelings you associate with each word.

1. The day was **crisp**—just perfect for taking a walk.

_____

2. The day was **raw**. How I wish I'd worn my gloves.

_____

3. Alicia is really **goofy**.

_____

4. Alicia is really **funny**.

_____

5. Juan was **thrifty** and saved his money.

_____

6. Juan was **cheap** and spent hardly any of his money.

_____

At Home: Together, discuss the connotations of the
following word pairs: *task, chore; say, announce; grab, take.*

A two-syllable word with the **VC/CV pattern** is usually divided between the two consonants.

swal low   wel come

The first syllable of a VC/CV word is a **closed** syllable. That means it has a short vowel sound and ends in a consonant.

Divide each word below into syllables. Write the syllables in the blanks provided.

1. copper _____ _____

2. member _____ _____

3. planner _____ _____

4. market _____ _____

5. summer _____ _____

6. slender _____ _____

7. fossil _____ _____

8. blanket _____ _____

9. fiction _____ _____

10. witness _____ _____

11. litter _____ _____

Which syllable is accented in these words?

12. _____

At Home: Ask the student to name three two-syllable words with the vowel-consonant-consonant-vowel pattern.

Because of Winn-Dixie
Grade 4/Unit 5

155

cranky	bumbling	selfish	exasperated
specialty	famished	commotion	

Choose a vocabulary word from the list that has the opposite meaning of the word(s) in dark type and makes each sentence true. Write it on the line.

1. Mariel is **happy** because she slept for only four hours last night.

   _____

2. I had only a bag of peanuts for lunch, so I was **stuffed** by the time

   dinner came. _____

3. The **graceful** waiter kept dropping and spilling everything.

   _____

4. It would be **generous** not to share your lunch with a hungry friend.

   _____

5. My mom felt **pleased** when I forgot to take out the garbage for the

   fourth time. _____

6. Tyler's dog caused a **peaceful pause** when it escaped and ran through

   a grocery store. _____

7. Knowing how to bake bread well is a real **inability**. _____

8. Use one of the vocabulary words in a sentence of your own.

   _____

© Macmillan/McGraw-Hill

As you read a story, think about what the characters do and say. This will help you **make judgments** about the plot and its characters.

Read the passage below. As you read, make judgments about the characters based on what they say and do. Then use your judgments to answer the questions below.

Carla's fourth grade class was planning a play. "I should be the princess," said Evelyn. "I am the best actress in class."

"No, I should," said Katerina. "I have the loudest voice and everyone will hear me."

Madison didn't say anything, but Carla could see that she wanted the part, too.

"Let's have tryouts," Carla suggested. "Everyone who wants to be the princess can read the same lines that the princess will say. Then the class can vote on who should have the part."

1. What kind of person do you think Evelyn is? _____

_____

2. What judgment can you make about Katerina?

_____

3. What kind of person is Madison? _____

_____

4. What kind of person is Carla? _____

_____

At Home: With the student, discuss a favorite movie or television show. Take turns making judgments about the characters.

**As you read *Ranita, the Frog Princess*, fill in the
Make Judgments Flow Chart.**

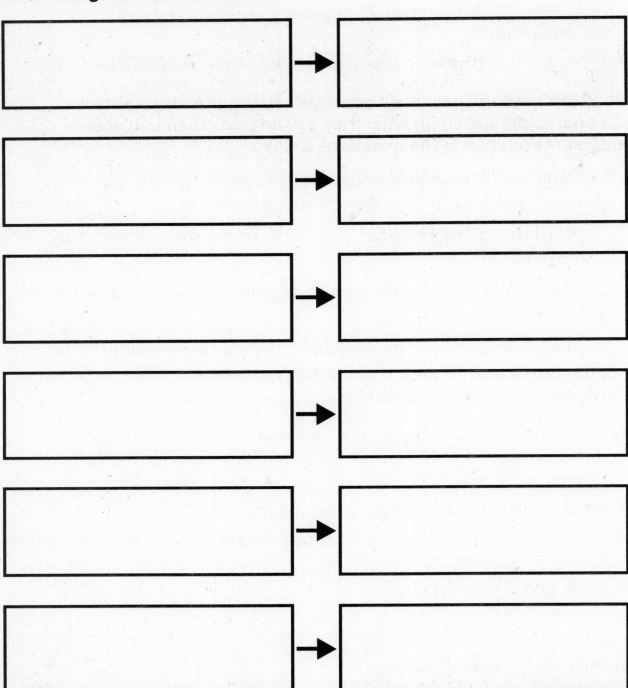

How does the information you wrote in the Make Judgments Flow Chart
help you to evaluate *Ranita, the Frog Princess*?

At Home: Have the student use the chart to retell the story.

Name _____

As I read, I will pay attention to dialogue and characters' roles.

	[Dean Dragon's kitchen. Matthew is struggling to light a
9	*fire with a match under a cauldron of stew. Dean Dragon*
20	*steps up and lights it with his dragon breath. Priscilla uses*
31	*a large wooden spoon to stir the stew, while Matthew*
41	*starts chopping carrots.]*
44	**Princess Priscilla:** *(inhaling a spoonful of stew with a*
53	*look of pleasure)* Mmm. That smells good already.
61	**Matthew:** Wait until it's finished. It's delicious.
68	**Dean Dragon:** *(smiling)* My vegetable stew is good, if
77	I do say so myself. It's famous among dragons.
86	**Princess Priscilla:** I can see why. *(She smiles at Dean,*
96	*then goes back to stirring the stew.)* I'd just like to get my
109	hands on that Knight Never-Do-Well. He woke me up in
121	the middle of the night and told me that my family was in
134	danger. So of course I came. Then when we got here, he tied
147	me to the tree and told me not to worry, he'd be back to
161	rescue me soon. I'd like to take a can opener to that shiny
174	armor of his. 177

Comprehension Check

1. Do you think Knight Never-Do-Well is a reliable person? **Make Judgments**

2. Do these characters enjoy working together? Why? **Make Inferences**

	Words Read	–	Number of Errors	=	Words Correct Score
First Read		–		=	
Second Read		–		=	

At Home: Help the student read the passage, paying
attention to the goal at the top of the page.

An **interview** is an account of the **questions** asked by one person and the **answers** given by another.

Read the following interview and then answer the questions.

As a reporter for the local newspaper, I recently met with Harry Buck. This ten-year-old is performing in a play put on by our local community theater. Here's part of the interview.

Q: What's the name of the play you are performing in?
A: It's called *Columbus Sails for the New World*.

Q: What part are you playing?
A: I'm playing Christopher Columbus.

Q: Did you have to audition for the role? If so, how many people tried out for it?
A: Yes, I had to audition. I think 4 or 5 of us tried out for the role.

Q: Can anyone try out for a play at the community theater?
A: Yes. We've put on plays with kids as young as 5 and adults as old as 70.

Q: How often do you rehearse?
A: For this play, we practice three nights a week and on the weekends.

1. Who is being interviewed? _____

_____

2. What role is Harry playing? _____

_____

3. What does the **Q** stand for? _____

4. What does the **A** stand for? _____

At Home: Discuss who the student would like to interview if the person could be anyone in the world today. What questions would he or she ask?

Name _____

Words that have opposite meanings are called **antonyms**.
A word can have more than one antonym.

Word	**Antonyms**
glad	sad, unhappy
angry	calm, pleased

Draw lines to match each word in Column 1 with an antonym from Column 2.

Column 1	Column 2
1. selfish	**a.** full
2. hungry	**b.** calm
3. noisy	**c.** slow
4. speedy	**d.** unselfish
5. excited	**e.** quiet

In the blank, write an antonym for each underlined word.

6. My dad was <u>happy</u> _____ when he saw my report card.

7. The fabric of the cushion felt very <u>smooth</u> _____.

8. The light in the room was <u>dim</u> _____.

9. Thalia made a fruit salad with cherries that were so <u>sweet</u>

_____.

10. I looked out the window and saw <u>sunny</u> _____ weather.

© Macmillan/McGraw-Hill

At Home: Together, name an antonym for the word *friendly*, *peace*, or *happiness*.

Name _____

An **open syllable** ends with a long vowel sound. Open first syllables have the **V/CV pattern.**

A **closed syllable** ends with a consonant. The vowel sound is short. Closed first syllables may have the **VC/V pattern.**

Read the words below. Listen for the vowel sound in the first syllable and draw a slash to show where to divide each word. If you have doubts, look up the word in a dictionary. Then, on the line, write whether the first syllable is open or closed.

1. h a b i t _____

2. n e v e r _____

3. w i p e r _____

4. t a l e n t _____

5. r o b i n _____

6. m e t e r _____

7. c i d e r _____

8. l e v e l _____

9. p r o m i s e _____

10. f a m o u s _____

11. l i m i t _____

12. f i n i s h _____

At Home: Ask the student to explain why the first syllable of each word above is open or closed.

Choose a vocabulary word to replace the underlined word(s) in each sentence. Write the word on the line.

period	vessels	valuable	documenting	estimated

1. Columbus sailed three <u>ships</u> on his voyage to the New World.

   _____

2. Many explorers were looking for gold and other <u>priceless</u> objects.

   _____

3. A <u>length of time</u> of over three hundred years was spent exploring

   the New World. _____

4. Explorers <u>guessed at</u> how much food and what supplies they would

   need on their long journeys. _____

5. <u>Recording</u> everything that happened on a voyage required a lot of

   discipline. _____

Now write a sentence that uses two of the vocabulary words in context.

6. _____

   _____

   _____

> A **fact** is something known to be true or real. A fact can always be proved true.
> An **opinion** is a judgment one holds to be true, even though there are no facts to support that conclusion.

Read the passage below. Then write *fact* or *opinion* after each statement.

The Spanish explored Mexico and Peru in the 1500s. They looted the lands they explored and filled their ships to the brim with gold and treasure. The jewels they carried back to Spain were the most beautiful in the world.

Because of their valuable cargo, the treasure ships were prey for pirates. The ships usually traveled a route that took them through a stretch of water called "The Spanish Main." Some pirates claimed to have captured hundreds of treasure ships there.

1. The Spanish explored Mexico and Peru in the 1500s.

_____

2. The Spanish looted the lands they explored. _____

3. The jewels they carried back to Spain were the most beautiful in the

world. _____

4. The ships usually traveled a route that took them through "The Spanish

Main." _____

5. Some pirates claimed to have captured hundreds of treasure ships.

_____

At Home: With the student, talk about the day you each had. After each statement, decide whether it was a fact or an opinion.

© Macmillan/McGraw-Hill

As you read *Exploring the Undersea Territory,* fill in the Fact and Opinion Chart.

Facts	Opinions

How does the information you wrote in the Fact and Opinion Chart help you to evaluate *Exploring the Undersea Territory*?

At Home: Have the student use the chart to retell the story.

Exploring the Undersea Territory
Grade 4/Unit 5

165

As I read, I will pay attention to pronunciation of vocabulary words and other difficult words.

12	A coral reef is a shelf that runs along the coastlines of countries throughout the world. Coral reefs are found in
21	shallow, warm waters all over the world.
28	Among all these reefs, there is one that stands out. It is
40	the Great Barrier Reef along the coast of Australia. It is
51	remarkable for many reasons. One is its length—over 1,250
60	miles. It is the largest coral reef ecosystem in the world,
71	and the largest organic structure on the planet. It is also
82	home to numerous kinds of sea life.
89	About 40,000 years ago, the Aboriginal peoples were
96	the only humans living on the Australian continent. They
105	fished and hunted along parts of the Great Barrier Reef.
115	For a long **period** of time they were the only people who
127	knew the reef existed.
131	When sailors began to explore the world, their boats
140	sometimes hit the sharp coral that was under the water,
150	sinking their **vessels**. The reef remained a mystery. 158

Comprehension Check

1. What details support the idea that the Great Barrier Reef is remarkable? **Main Idea and Details**

2. Why were the sailors unaware of the coral reef? **Make Inferences**

	Words Read	–	Number of Errors	=	Words Correct Score
First Read		–		=	
Second Read		–		=	

At Home: Help the student read the passage, paying attention to the goal at the top of the page.

When you **skim,** you look quickly through a selection to find out what it is about. You look for its main idea and important details.

When you **scan,** you run your eyes through a text looking for a specific word or phrase. You don't read every word.

Read the information below. Then answer the questions that follow.

How to Scan for Information

When you scan for information, follow these steps.

- Identify the key words and phrases that you are looking for.
- Pass your eyes over each line of print quickly.
- Don't stop until you see your key word or phrase.
- Double-check to be sure that you have found the information.

1. Why would it not have been useful to skim the passage above the box?

_____

_____

_____

2. If you're looking for key words and phrases, are you skimming or

scanning? _____

3. Which of the following is the best key word or phrase that you would use for scanning?
   a. hammerhead   **b.** sharks   **c.** marine life

4. Which do you think is more useful, skimming or scanning? Explain your

answer. _____

_____

At Home: Together, skim a passage. Discuss what the
passage is about.

Exploring the Undersea Territory
Grade 4/Unit 5
167

An analogy shows how two pairs of words are related. The first pair of words has to be related to the second pair in the same way.

An example of an analogy is *hot* is to *summer* as *cold* is to *winter*.

Complete each analogy with a word from the box.

enormous	listening	submarine	evening	elated
ocean	sights	painter	expensive	furious

1. *Saltwater* is to _____ as *freshwater* is to *stream.*

2. *Breakfast* is to *morning* as *dinner* is to _____.

3. *Ship* is to *above water* as _____ is to *below water.*

4. *Camera* is to *photographer* as *paintbrush* is to _____.

5. *Big* is to _____ as *small* is to *tiny.*

6. *Watching* is to *movie* as _____ is to *music.*

7. *Sad* is to *miserable* as *angry* is to _____.

8. _____ are to *eyes* as *smells* are to *nose.*

Write two more analogies below.

9. _____ is to _____ as _____
   is to _____.

10. _____ is to _____ as _____
   is to _____.

At Home: Together, complete the following analogies: *Tires* is to *bicycle* as *wheels* are to *rollerskates. Many* is to *few* as *always* is to *never.*

When you say a two-syllable word, one of the syllables is pronounced with more emphasis. The syllable pronounced with more emphasis is the **accented syllable.**

In the word *between,* the second syllable is accented.

Word	First Syllable	Second Syllable
between	be	tween

cancel	remind	frosty	behave	tender
action	chamber	gather	belief	confuse
contain	certain	mustang	convince	damage

Say each word from the list above aloud. Then sort the words into two groups: words with an accented first syllable and words with an accented second syllable.

First Syllable Accented

_____

_____

_____

_____

_____

_____

_____

Second Syllable Accented

_____

_____

_____

_____

_____

_____

_____

© Macmillan/McGraw-Hill

At Home: Take turns saying the following words: *carpet, dentist, demand, noble.* Decide whether the accent in each word is on the first or second syllable.

strutting	swarms	flicked	barbecue
skyscrapers	glorious	collage	

Answer each question, substituting the vocabulary word for its underlined definition.

1. Have you seen Jason? Why was he <u>walking in a proud manner</u> down the hall?

   _____

2. Why were there <u>great numbers</u> of people at the mall?

   _____

3. Did the horse get you when she <u>snapped</u> her tail?

   _____

4. What kinds of food do you like to eat at an <u>outdoor gathering at which meat is roasted over an open fire and served</u>?

   _____

5. Where can you go to see <u>very tall buildings</u>?

   _____

6. How would you describe an <u>exceedingly beautiful or splendid</u> day?

   _____

7. What materials are you using to make that <u>artistic composition made by pasting or gluing materials together on a surface</u>?

   _____

Use two of the words above in one sentence.

8. _____

Characters are the people, and sometimes animals, that you read about in a story. The main character is the story's most important character. You can learn about characters from the things they say, do, and feel.

Read the following passage. Then answer the questions that follow.

Brian said to his mom, "I'm worried about going to art camp. I won't know anyone there."

"Don't worry about it," his mom said. "You'll see. It'll be fine."

When Brian walked into the camp meeting room, he swallowed hard. Most of the tables were full of kids talking and laughing with each other. There was only one spot open, and it was at a table way in the back.

There were three other kids at the table—Alex, Kenya, and Mike. They all knew each other, but they were happy to talk to Brian, too. The four of them wound up working on a project together. By the time Brian went home, he knew he had a new set of friends for the summer.

1. Who is the main character? _____

2. Name the other characters in the story.

_____

3. What kind of person do you think Brian is? _____

_____

_____

4. Do you think that Alex, Kenya, and Mike are friendly? Explain your answer.

_____

_____

At Home: Together, read a story. Then identify the main character and discuss what he or she is like. Use examples from the story to support your description.

Me and Uncle Romie
Grade 4/Unit 5

171

Name _____

As you read *Me and Uncle Romie,* fill in the Character Web.

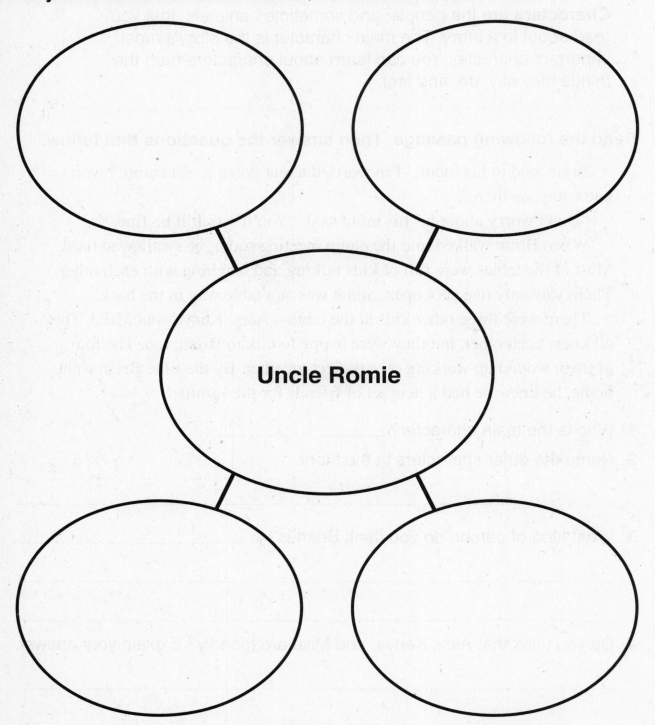

Uncle Romie

How does the information you wrote in the Character Web help you to
monitor your comprehension of *Me and Uncle Romie*?

At Home: Have the student use the chart to retell the story.

Name _____

As I read, I will pay attention to my tempo in order to match the action in the story.

	Carly held her breath as the broad-tailed hummingbird
8	fluttered near the cluster of wildflowers. She stared into
17	her camera, waiting. A fly landed on Carly's arm. She
27	**flicked** it away with a finger. The bird flew near a flower.
39	The flower wasn't red enough, though. Carly waited.
47	The bird flew to another flower. This one was too small.
58	Finally, the bird hesitated over the largest, reddest flower.
67	Carly began to snap pictures. She was certain that these
77	would be some of the best pictures she had ever taken.
88	Carly raced home and uploaded the pictures onto her
97	computer. She couldn't wait to see the results.
105	But when the pictures came up on the screen, she was
116	disappointed. Carly studied them, then opened her photo
124	journal. She wrote: "Hummingbird pictures: The bird's
131	wings are a blur, not enough detail on flower, bird isn't
142	close enough to the flower in any shot. Why aren't these
153	the way I thought they would be?" 160

Comprehension Check

1. What do you learn about Carly in this passage? **Character**

2. How might the journal help Carly take better pictures in the future? **Draw Conclusions**

	Words Read	–	Number of Errors	=	Words Correct Score
First Read		–		=	
Second Read		–		=	

At Home: Help the student read the passage, paying attention to the goal at the top of the page.

Me and Uncle Romie
Grade 4/Unit 5

173

© Macmillan/McGraw-Hill

Name _____

Directions explain how to do something. Sometimes numbered steps are given to tell the reader the order in which things should be done. **Sequence words,** such as *first, then, next,* and *last,* can also help readers follow directions. Sometimes a list of needed **materials** is included in the directions.

Read the following directions. Then answer the questions.

How to Paint a Room

Materials

paint	drop cloth	paint stirrer	roller
painter's tape	paintbrushes	paint tray	

Directions

1. Put drop cloths on the floor and furniture to protect them.
2. Place blue painter's tape around the areas that you do not want painted, like windows, for instance.
3. Open the paint cans and mix the paint with a stirrer.
4. Pour the paint into a paint tray. Use a roller to paint the walls.
5. Use a paintbrush to paint the corners, edges, and other spots the roller can't reach.
6. When you are finished, wash the brushes and rollers with warm water.

1. How many materials are needed to paint a room? ____

2. What is the first thing you should do before you paint a room?

   _____

3. What do you pour the paint into? _____

4. What would happen if you skipped Step 2?

   _____

© Macmillan/McGraw-Hill

At Home: Together, write step-by-step directions on how to paint or decorate something you have made.

Context clues can help readers determine the meaning of an unfamiliar word. Sometimes writers use description to help readers define unfamiliar words.

Underline the context clues that describe the meaning of the boldfaced word. Then write the word's definition.

1. We decided that the **theme** of our collage would be what we did during our vacation.

   Definition: _____

2. The chef felt her masterpiece was not complete until she **shredded** cheese into tiny strips and sprinkled it on top of the omelette.

   Definition: _____

3. The young artist worked with many different **mediums**— oil and acrylic paints, colored pencils, and chalk.

   Definition: _____

4. My neighbor offered me the **proposition** of getting $20 each time it snows for shoveling his stairs and sidewalk.

   Definition: _____

5. My two uncles are starting a business together as **joint** owners.

   Definition: _____

6. After we paid our **admission,** we could enter the museum and stay as long as we wished.

   Definition: _____

© Macmillan/McGraw-Hill

At Home: Together, read a story. Then try to figure out the meanings of unfamiliar words by looking for context clues in surrounding text.

The schwa + *r* or /ər/ sound is what you hear at the end of *coll<u>ar</u>, dang<u>er</u>,* and *vict<u>or</u>.* Notice that this sound can be spelled in three different ways—*ar, er,* and *or.*

| barber | zipper | anchor | harbor | popular | collar |

Use the words in the box to complete each sentence. Underline the letters that make the /ər/ sound in each word.

1. Every time my clever _____ cuts my hair, he creates a work of art.

2. The Flemish oil paintings in the north tower are the most

    _____ exhibit in the museum.

3. My favorite collage is the one I made with the _____ from an old pair of trousers.

4. Aunt Susie finished her watercolor painting of the clipper ships in the

    _____.

5. I put a _____ and leash on my dog when we go for a walk in the park.

6. Uncle Tim thinks the old rusty tanker _____ in his front yard is beautiful!

Now look for other examples of the /ər/ sound in the sentences and underline them as well.

At Home: Take turns making up a sentence for each of the words in the box.

© Macmillan/McGraw-Hill

descendants	habitat	threatened	sanctuary
coaxing	fragile	glistening	

Label each statement _True_ or _False_. If the statement is false, explain why.

1. Something is _fragile_ if it is hard to break.

   _____

2. The desert is the whale's natural _habitat_.

   _____

3. When you try to force someone strongly to do something, you are _coaxing_ them.

   _____

4. Children are _descendants_ of their grandparents.

   _____

5. If you think you are safe from harm, you may feel _threatened_.

   _____

6. A _sanctuary_ is a place where wild animals can live safely.

   _____

7. When clouds are blocking the sun, the ocean water is _glistening_.

   _____

8. Write a sentence that contains two of the above vocabulary words.

   _____

Name _____

A **cause** makes something else happen. When you ask the question "Why did that happen?" the answer is the cause. What happens as a result of the cause is its **effect**. When you ask the question "What happened?" the answer is the effect.

Read the passage below. Then answer the questions that follow.

Every spring my family goes on a camping trip. My parents like to get out of the city, and they want my brother and me to enjoy nature. When we first leave the city I'm always surprised by the quiet. There are no more sirens or blaring horns because there is no traffic.

Since we love to "rough it," we bring only what we really need. We have sleeping bags, cooking equipment, and food. We set up camp near a mountain river. Because the river water comes from melting snow, we keep food that can spoil in a container in the water. We put a big rock on top so our food doesn't float away.

Our week in the mountains is fun for the entire family. It brings us together and, for a little while, we forget about our hectic city lives. We all look forward to our yearly camping trip when we all slow down and enjoy the peace and beauty of nature.

1. What causes the family to go on a camping trip every spring?

_____

2. What is the effect of driving where there is no traffic?

_____

3. What causes the river's cold temperature? _____

4. What effect does the yearly camping trip have on the family?

_____

© Macmillan/McGraw-Hill

At Home: Together, talk about causes and effects that you can observe in your daily lives.

Name _____

As you read *Wild Horses*, fill in the Cause and Effect Diagram.

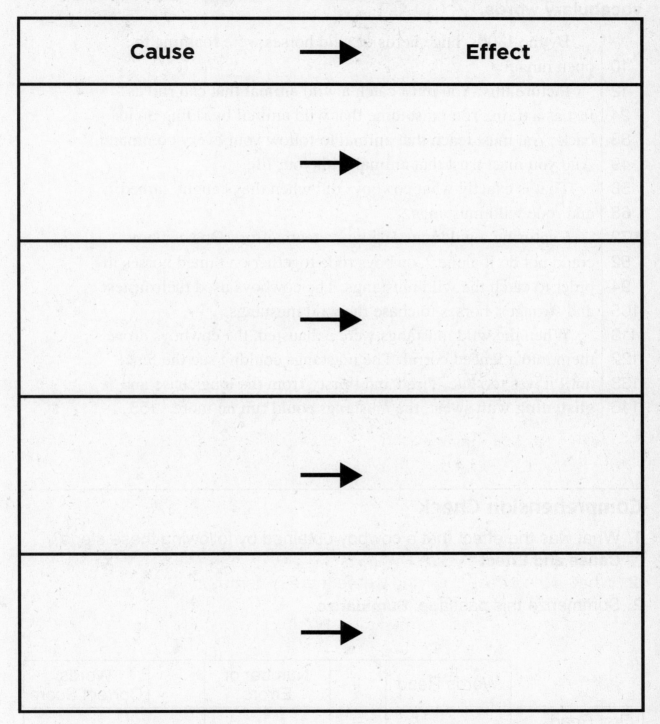

Cause	→	Effect
	→	
	→	
	→	
	→	

How does the information you wrote in the Cause and Effect Diagram
help you to monitor your comprehension of *Wild Horses*?

At Home: Have the student use the chart to retell the story.

As I read, I will pay attention to my pronunciation of vocabulary words.

	By the 1800s, huge herds of wild horses were roaming the
10	open range.
12	Picture this: You must catch a wild animal that can run as
24	fast as a train. You must tame that wild animal by riding on its
38	back. You must teach that animal to follow your every command.
49	And you must trust that animal with your life.
58	That is exactly what cowboys did when they caught, tamed,
68	and rode wild mustangs.
72	Capturing a wild mustang was a team effort. One cowboy
82	could not do it alone. Cowboys rode together on tamed horses in
94	order to catch the wild mustangs. The cowboys used their fastest
105	and strongest horses to chase the wild mustangs.
113	When the wild mustangs were exhausted, the cowboys drove
122	them into a fenced corral. The mustangs couldn't see the fence
133	until it was too late. Tired and thirsty from the long chase and
146	**glistening** with sweat, the mustangs could run no more. 155

Comprehension Check

1. What was the effect that a cowboy obtained by following these steps?
   Cause and Effect

2. Summarize this passage. **Summarize**

	Words Read	–	Number of Errors	=	Words Correct Score
First Read		–		=	
Second Read		–		=	

© Macmillan/McGraw-Hill

At Home: Help the student read the passage, paying attention to the goal at the top of the page.

Name _____

A **figure of speech** is a way to use vivid or poetic language to express oneself.
Example: The thirsty earth soaked up the rain.
When the figure of speech is an extreme exaggeration, it is called **hyperbole**.
Example: She was dying of thirst by the end of the tennis match.

Read the following sentences. Put an X over those that have no figures of speech. For those that do, underline them. When the figure of speech is hyperbole, put a check in the box.

1. The runaway mare stood there calmly, munching the long grass and allowing the men with the lassoes to get a little bit closer. ☐

2. Timothy was as strong as a horse. ☐

3. Our team's best batter hit that ball into the next county. ☐

4. When Jim asked his father whether he could stay out until midnight, he never expected his dad to bite his head off. ☐

5. Jim's dad got hopping mad. He really blew his top! ☐

6. Jim's older brother asked him if he wanted him to speak to their dad, but Jim told him not to stick his neck out. ☐

7. Omar winked and said, "We're having ice cream cake at the party, but keep it under your hat." ☐

8. Rather than preparing a speech for Open House, Samantha thought she would play it by ear. ☐

9. Roger would give his right arm for a new skateboard. ☐

10. Pedro's great-grandmother is older than the hills. ☐

© Macmillan/McGraw-Hill

At Home: Read and discuss together the meanings of the figures of speech above.

Context clues can help readers determine the meaning of unfamiliar words. Sometimes, you can gather context clues by reading the paragraph in which an unfamiliar word appears.

A. Read the passage below. Use context clues to help you figure out the meanings of the words in dark type.

We were standing around the **corral**, leaning on the fence and watching the horses. "Midnight's a good mother," I said, as the black mare's **foal** followed closely behind her. Only two days old, it was still getting used to walking on its long, **wobbly** legs.

My aunt sighed. "Sometimes I wonder if they would have been better off in the canyon, living in the **wilderness** instead of around people," she said.

B. Write the definition for each word, along with the context clues that helped you identify the word's meaning.

1. corral   definition: _____

context clues: _____

2. foal   definition: _____

context clues: _____

3. wobbly   definition: _____

context clues: _____

4. wilderness   definition: _____

context clues: _____

© Macmillan/McGraw-Hill

At Home: Together, read a magazine article or newspaper story. Use context clues to define unfamiliar words.

Name _____

The /əl/ sound is what you hear at the end of *double, medal, vessel,* and *fossil*. Notice the four different letter pairs that can stand for the sound.

local	little	adaptable	channel	pupil
kettle	verbal	uncle	natural	

Choose a word from the box to fill in each blank. Underline the letters that make the /əl/ sound in each word.

1. A _____ community group is working to protect the

   _____ habitat of wild horses.

2. _____ Cal, my grandfather's brother, used to work on a
   farm that caught and tamed wild horses.

3. For homework, the _____ watched a documentary about

   wild horses on the nature _____.

4. Wild horses are not the most _____ animals, which makes
   them difficult to tame.

5. When working with horses, the trainer would call out _____
   commands.

6. I poured a _____ more water from the _____
   into my tea cup.

At Home: Together with the student, choose two other
words from the box and use them in sentences. Identify the
/əl/ spelling of the words you chose.

Wild Horses
Grade 4/Unit 5

183

© Macmillan/McGraw-Hill

A. Answer each question using the underlined vocabulary word.

1. What have you done to make someone feel <u>exasperated</u>?

   _____

2. If you are <u>documenting</u> something, what are you doing?

   _____

3. Where are you likely to find <u>skyscrapers</u>?

   _____

4. How would you describe the <u>habitat</u> of a polar bear?

   _____

5. Where is there often a lot of <u>commotion</u>?

   _____

B. Read each vocabulary word. Then draw a line to the word that has the opposite meaning.

Column 1

6. fragile

7. positive

8. valuable

9. cranky

10. estimated

Column 2

a. exact

b. pleasant

c. unsure

d. sturdy

e. worthless

C. Write the vocabulary word that means almost the same thing as the underlined word or words.

| strutting | coaxing | peculiar | famished | glistening |

11. I thought the artist's style was rather <u>strange</u>. _____

12. Larry was <u>very hungry</u> and couldn't wait for lunch. _____

13. Kim was <u>walking proudly</u> down the hall after getting an "A" on her test.

_____

14. The <u>sparkling</u> sunlight on the water made the ocean look as if it were

filled with diamonds. _____

15. <u>Convincing</u> a toddler to eat isn't always easy. _____

D. Write the vocabulary word that completes each sentence.

| selfish | swarms | vessels | bumbling | threatened |

16. The _____ princess never thought of anyone but herself.

17. When most lizards feel _____ they hurry to the nearest
hiding place.

18. The captain hoped to find treasure in the _____ that lay
for so many centuries on the bottom of the sea.

19. When my sister tried the advanced dance class, she felt like a

_____ beginner.

20. In the summer, _____ of people head to the beach.

annoyed	prospectors	outstretched	circular
glinted	reference	disappointment	

A. Draw a line to match the vocabulary word to its meaning.

1. reference

2. prospectors

3. disappointment

4. annoyed

5. circular

6. outstretched

7. glinted

a. reaching out

b. sparkled

c. round, like a circle

d. upset

e. people who search for gold

f. the feeling when something doesn't happen the way you hoped it would

g. a source of reliable information

B. Write a paragraph or two using as many of the vocabulary words as possible.

_____

_____

_____

_____

_____

_____

_____

© Macmillan/McGraw-Hill

A **cause** is what makes something happen. If you can answer the question "Why did that happen?" then you know the cause.

What happens as a result of the cause is the **effect.** If you can answer the question "What happened?" then you know the effect.

Read the passage below. As you read, think about causes and effects. Then answer the questions.

Sam Brannan was a merchant in San Francisco. When he heard that gold had been found near the American River, he knew just what to do. He bought up every pickax, shovel, and pan in the entire city. Then he ran through the streets of San Francisco spreading the news about the discovery of gold.

Because Brannan was the only merchant who had tools to sell, he could charge as much as he wanted. Prospectors were willing to spend $15.00 for a pan that was worth only 60 cents. It wasn't long before Brannan became one of the richest men in California—without ever panning for gold!

1. What caused Sam Brannan to buy up all the mining tools?

_____

2. What was the effect of Brannan's spreading the news about gold?

_____

3. What caused miners to pay $15.00 for a 60-cent pan? _____

_____

4. What was the effect of so many prospectors buying Brannan's tools?

_____

At Home: Talk about the string of effects that might be caused by oversleeping on a school day.

As you read *The Gold Rush Game,* fill in the Cause and Effect
Diagram.

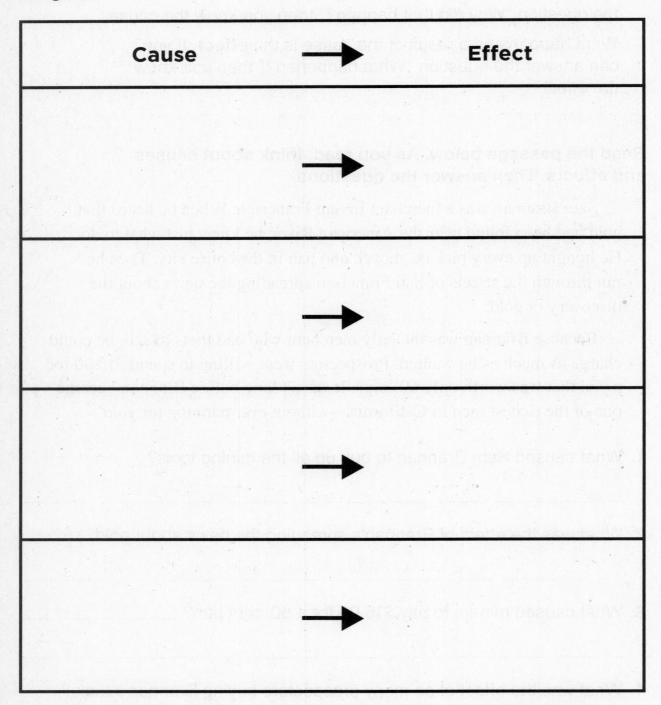

Cause	→	Effect

How does the information you wrote in the Cause and Effect Diagram
help you to analyze the story structure of *The Gold Rush Game*?

At Home: Have the student use the chart to retell the story.

As I read, I will pay attention to pauses, stops, and intonation.

	In the early 1800s, the United States needed room to grow.
10	Most people lived in the East. The cities were crowded. New land
22	was expensive. Young families couldn't afford to buy farms.
31	Then the United States government purchased land from
39	France. The government also acquired land from Mexico. Soon the
49	country stretched all the way to the Pacific Ocean. People looked
60	to the setting sun with **outstretched** arms and said, "Go west!"
71	Settlers rode in wagons or on horses. They followed long, dusty
82	trails across hot plains for thousands of miles. There was no shelter.
94	People slept in tents on the ground. They had to watch out for wild
108	animals like wolves and snakes. The trip west could take months.
119	Then a railroad was built that stretched from the East Coast
130	almost to the West Coast. The railroad made travel faster. More
141	people poured into the new lands. The settlers quickly built small
152	towns where the farming, fishing, and mining were good. 161

Comprehension Check

1. What caused people to move west? **Cause and Effect**

2. What does the author feel towards people who lived in the East in the 1800s? **Author's Perspective**

	Words Read	−	Number of Errors	=	Words Correct Score
First Read		−		=	
Second Read		−		=	

At Home: Help the student read the passage, paying attention to the goal at the top of the page.

Name _____

A **timeline** is a visual way to show a sequence of events in a
period of time. Events that happened during that time period
are placed on the timeline in the order in which they happened.

Statehood Timeline

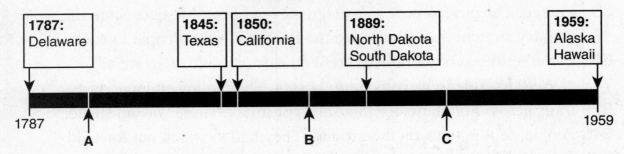

1787:
Delaware

1845:
Texas

1850:
California

1889:
North Dakota
South Dakota

1959:
Alaska
Hawaii

1787

A

B

C

1959

Use the timeline to answer the questions.

1. What is the subject of this timeline?

_____

_____

2. When did Texas become a state? _____

3. Which states became states in 1889? _____

_____

4. How many years does the timeline cover? _____

5. Arizona and New Mexico became states in 1912. Where would you put

that event on the timeline:—at point A, point B, or point C? _____

6. What is the earliest date on this timeline? The latest date? _____

© Macmillan/McGraw-Hill

At Home: Together, make a timeline of the student's
own life. Show one event for every year or two of life.

Name _____

> A **suffix** is a word part that can be added to the end of a **base word.** Adding a suffix to a base word changes its meaning. When added to the end of a verb, the suffix *-er* or *-or* means "a person who."
>
> teach + er = teacher (a person who teaches)
> act + or = actor (a person who acts)

Look for the verb. Then add the correct suffix to make a word that means the same as the entire phrase in bold.

1. **A person who travels** across time is a time _____.

2. **A person who mines** for gold is a _____.

3. In the 1800s, many people traveled by sea. And **a person who worked**

   on the sailing ships was called a _____.

4. Wong Daido was a **person who survived** the river current.

   He was a _____.

5. **A person who settled** in California was a _____.

6. **A person who bikes** on California's mountain trails is a mountain

   _____.

7. **A person who visits** the site of Sutter's Mill is a _____.

8. **A person who researches** the history of the California Gold Rush

   is a _____.

At Home: Together, think of other words that have the suffix *-er* or *-or* and mean "a person who."

The Gold Rush Game
Grade 4/Unit 6   191

The final /ən/ sound is what you hear at the end of the following words:

wooden   *often*   *raisin*   *reason*   *bacon*

The /ən/ sound can be spelled *-en, -in,* or *-on.*

bacon	proven	button	eleven	cousin	dozen
women	reason	shaken	listen	common	cotton

Write a word from the box to complete each sentence. Underline the letters that represent the /ən/ sound.

1. Were there any _____ at the mining camps?

2. Nine plus two is one less than a _____.

3. Do you know the _____ why the computer turned into a time machine?

4. Miners fried up lots of _____ for their breakfasts.

5. General stores in San Francisco sold yards of _____ for all the clothes the miners would need.

6. My great-grandfather had a _____ who was a gold miner.

7. The earthquake left them feeling very _____ up.

8. I love to _____ to stories about the Gold Rush.

9. Most of the miners could sew a patch or a _____ on their clothes.

10. The pigeon is a _____ bird in many cities.

© Macmillan/McGraw-Hill

At Home: Think of and write as many /ən/ words as possible in two minutes.

Name _____

| eavesdropping | scuffling | wistfully | logical |
| jumble | scornfully | acquaintance | |

Answer the questions using a vocabulary word that means the same as the underlined word or phrase.

1. Did the raccoon leave a <u>big mess</u> when it turned over the garbage can?

_____

2. Was the seagull gazing <u>hopefully</u> at the crab on the rocks below?

_____

3. Was the owl in the tree <u>listening in</u> on your conversation by the campfire?

_____

4. What do you think is making that <u>scraping or dragging</u> sound in the woods?

_____

5. Is it <u>reasonable</u> to expect an animal to act like a person?

_____

6. Would a mouse be the <u>not-too-close friend</u> of a cat in real life?

_____

7. Would an owl look at a wolf with <u>dislike and disrespect</u>?

_____

8. Use two of the vocabulary words in a sentence about a wild animal.

_____

A **theme** is the subject, or topic, that an author is writing about. To identify a story's theme, ask yourself, "What is the subject of this story?"

Read the passage. As you read, think about the theme. Then answer the questions that follow.

Mario Mouse did not always do as he was told. His mother had told him never to leave the safety of their mouse hole, because the world outside was dangerous. But Mario was an adventurous mouse. One evening he ran out of the hole to see the world.

My, the world was big! He found himself in a huge room. It had chairs, a couch, and low tables. In one corner, he saw a big box that had bright pictures and spoke! Mario crept forward to look at the bright pictures.

Just then a big furry animal bounded into the room, making snarling noises. Mario was terrified. He let out a squeak and scurried back to his mouse hole. He dove through it, back to safety. "Mom was so right," he thought.

1. What is one of the themes of this story? _____

_____

_____

2. On the lines below, list three story events that support the theme that you identified.

a. _____

b. _____

c. _____

At Home: Discuss the themes of some of your favorite movies.

As you read *The Cricket in Times Square*, fill in the Theme Map.

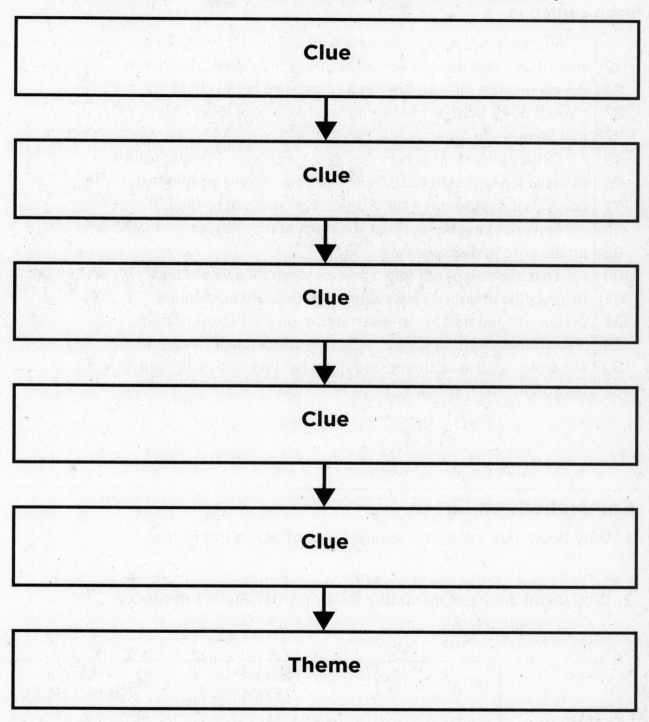

Clue

Clue

Clue

Clue

Clue

Theme

How does the information you wrote in the Theme Map help you to
analyze the story structure of *The Cricket in Times Square*?

 At Home: Have the student use the chart to retell the story.

The Cricket in Times Square
Grade 4/Unit 6
195

Name _____

As I read, I will pay attention to end punctuation in each sentence.

12	Stripes raised his eyes and blinked at Jani. He was a lovely striped cat. Jani thought he looked like a little tiger. She picked
24	the cat up. She sat with him on a chair, stroking his head.
37	"You'll never believe what we learned in school today," she
47	told Stripes.
49	Stripes looked up at her with wise green eyes. "People used
60	to make leopard-skin coats," she told him. "Some people still
71	do. A coat made from a cat, Stripes. It makes me so mad!"
84	Jani could not be sure, but she thought that Stripes scrunched
95	up his nose in disgust.
100	That night, Jani fell into a restless sleep. She tossed and
111	turned. She dreamed about animals who could talk. In her
121	dream, she hid nearby, **eavesdropping** on their conversation.
129	The animals were in danger. And they needed help. Suddenly
139	she woke up. It was almost midnight, but there was a light in
152	her room. "Who's there?" she asked. 158

Comprehension Check

1. Why does Jani fall into a restless sleep? **Make Inferences**

2. Why might Jani feel sympathy for leopards? **Make Inferences**

	Words Read	–	Number of Errors	=	Words Correct Score
First Read		–		=	
Second Read		–		=	

© Macmillan/McGraw-Hill

At Home: Help the student read the passage, paying attention to the goal at the top of the page.

Advertisements use pictures and text to get people to buy or do something. Advertisements use several techniques of persuasion:

• loaded language, such as *best, better,* and *special*
• bandwagon, or urging that you join many other people
• testimonials, or the backing of a celebrity
• warnings that the offer is good for a limited time only

Read each advertisement. Then answer the questions.

Our world-class bird feeder will blow you away! It's the best there is. As Bob Wells of the Nature Channel says, "You won't find a better feeder anywhere."

1. What techniques does the advertisement use? _____

2. What words or phrases did you use to figure out the advertisement's

   approach? _____

Join your friends and neighbors by donating to the Save the Tigers fund. Act now and receive this beautiful tote bag.

3. What techniques does the advertisement use? _____

4. What words or phrases did you use to figure out the advertisement's

   approach? _____

At Home: Discuss the techniques used by your favorite or least favorite television ads.

The Cricket in Times Square
Grade 4/Unit 6
197

Context clues are words in the same or surrounding sentences that help a reader figure out the meaning of an unfamiliar word.

Read the passage below. Then write the meaning of each word in dark type and the context clues that helped you figure it out.

The **audience streamed** into the theater to hear Regina Jackson's talk. Hundreds of people moved smoothly but quickly into their seats. Jackson was the world's leading **authority** on **jaguars.** No one else knew more than she did about the lives of these big cats. From the moment she began to speak everyone sat quietly. You could see by their interested expressions that they were **fascinated** by what she had to say. When Regina finished, everyone stood up and began to applaud.

1. audience   Definition: _____

Context clues: _____

2. streamed   Definition: _____

Context clues: _____

3. authority   Definition: _____

Context clues: _____

4. jaguars   Definition: _____

Context clues: _____

5. fascinated   Definition: _____

Context clues: _____

At Home: Give the student a word. Then have him or her write a sentence with clues that provide context to the word's meaning.

Name _____

> **Homophones** are words that sound the same but are spelled differently and have different meanings. The words *right* and *write* are homophones.
>
> right = correct   write = make marks on paper

Fill in each blank with the correct homophone.

1. **tale / tail**   He told a _____ about a lion that lost its

   _____.

2. **patience / patients**   The doctor encouraged his _____

   to have more _____ while they waited to see him.

3. **dough / doe**   The _____ and her fawns ate the

   _____ that the baker left on the window sill.

4. **wade / weighed**   She tried to _____ across the river

   wearing a backpack that _____ ninety pounds.

5. **bolder / boulder**   The skier grew _____ after he

   jumped over the _____.

6. **plain / plane**   We flew in a _____ over the

   _____ where the buffalo were.

7. **week / weak**   I felt _____ for a _____.

8. **aloud / allowed**   "There are no photos _____," the

   guide said _____.

At Home: Together, think of as many other homophone pairs as you can.

| fossil | inspected | paleontologist | stumbled upon |

Write a vocabulary word to replace the underlined words in each sentence below. Then make up a sentence that includes the word.

1. The team <u>looked carefully at</u> _____ the sunken ship.

_____

_____

2. Researchers <u>came unexpectedly to</u> _____ a brilliant conclusion.

_____

_____

3. The <u>scientist who studied things from millions of years ago</u>

_____ knew that what looked like a stick of wood was really an ancient bone.

_____

_____

4. The <u>preserved remains</u> _____ of two ants in amber proved that the insect has not changed much over the past 90 million years.

_____

_____

A **generalization** is a broad statement about something. Based on certain facts or instances, a general rule is formed. This general rule may not always be true each time that it is applied. Most generalizations that are true use words such as *many, most,* and *usually.* If a generalization uses words such as *all, none,* or *never,* the statement may be too broad to be true.

> **True:** Many dinosaurs were meat-eaters.
> **Not True:** All dinosaurs were meat-eaters.

Read the facts. Then write a generalization that is true, based on the facts presented and on what you already know.

1. • Eagles, wrens, cardinals, hawks, and robins are birds that can fly.

   • Gulls, crows, condors, bluejays, and egrets are birds that can fly.

   • Ostriches are birds that can't fly.

   _____

2. • Dinosaur fossils have been found in North and South America.

   • Dinosaur fossils have been found in Europe and Asia.

   • Dinosaur fossils have been found in Africa and Australia.

   _____

3. • Tyrannosaurus rex was about 40 feet long.

   • Brachiosaurus was about 70 feet long.

   • Compsognathus was about the size of a chicken.

   _____

4. • Mrs. Vega's fourth-grade class loves to read about dinosaurs.

   • Ms. Kim's fourth-grade class loves to read about dinosaurs.

   • Some fourth graders in my class are not very interested in dinosaurs.

   _____

At Home: Together, discuss the generalizations above. How might you reword each generalization to make the sentence false?

© Macmillan/McGraw-Hill

As you read *Meet a Bone-ified Explorer,* fill in the Generalizations Chart.

Information from Text	What I Know	Generalization

© Macmillan/McGraw-Hill

How does the information you wrote in this Generalizations Chart help you analyze the text structure of *Meet a Bone-ified Explorer*?

At Home: Have the student use the chart to retell the story.

Name _____

As I read, I will pay attention to the pronunciation of vocabulary and other difficult words.

	Thousands of years ago pharaohs ruled the great kingdom
9	of Egypt. When pharaohs died, they were buried in tombs
19	with their treasures. One of these pharaohs was very young.
29	His name was King Tutankhamen (TOOT-ahngk-ah-muhn).
34	The entrance to Tutankhamen's tomb was well hidden.
42	The Egyptians built tombs that were hard to find and even
53	harder to enter. They made secret entrances and false passages.
63	Soon after the king was buried, robbers broke into the
73	tomb and took some of the treasures. The tomb was then
84	resealed. It stayed buried in the sand for thousands of years.
95	In the early 1900s, an Englishman named Lord Carnarvon
103	began the search for this pharoah's tomb. Carnarvon believed
112	that the king was buried in the Valley of the Kings.
123	In 1907, Carnarvon began working with a man named
131	Howard Carter. Carter was an artist for **paleontologists**.
139	He made drawings of the **fossils** and other findings. Carter
149	and Carnarvon began a search for King Tutankhamen's
157	tomb. It was a search that would last for many years. 168

Comprehension Check

1. How do you know that the two men were dedicated in their search for the tomb? **Draw Conclusions**

2. Why did the Egyptians build tombs that were hard to find? **Cause and Effect**

	Words Read	–	Number of Errors	=	Words Correct Score
First Read		–		=	
Second Read		–		=	

At Home: Help the student read the passage, paying attention to the goal at the top of the page.

For items 1–12, read the passage and fill in the information asked for in the form. Then answer the questions that follow.

Mr. Carter's fourth-grade class plans to visit the York Science Museum on Friday, April 22. The bus will leave at 8:00 A.M. and return at 4:00 P.M. Students should bring a bag lunch on the day of the trip. Permission forms must be returned to Mr. Carter by Friday, April 8.

Field Trip Permission Form

1. Student's Name _____ 2. Date of trip _____

3. Student's Address _____

_____

4. Home Phone # _____

5. Destination _____

6. Transportation by ☐ Bus ☐ Car ☐ Subway

7. Time Departing _____ 8. Time Returning _____

9. Parent's Name _____

10. ☐ I give permission for my son/daughter to go.

11. Parent's Signature _____

12. Today's Date _____

13. Should the student write in the space next to item 11 on the form? Explain why.

_____

14. What is the latest date that should appear in the space next to item 12?

_____

At Home: Together, discuss the different kinds of forms that you have used recently.

Many English words are formed by adding word parts, such as prefixes and suffixes, to a basic word, or root word. Many words have roots that come from Latin, the language of ancient Rome.

- All words that have the root *aud-* have something to do with sound or hearing.
- All words that have the root *spec-* have something to do with sight or seeing.

Complete each sentence with a word from the box that takes the place of the underlined words.

audible	audio	audience	spectacles	spectator	spectacular

1. From the back of the auditorium, we could hardly hear the <u>part that can be heard</u> portion of the paleontologist's presentation. _____

2. A <u>person who watches</u> at the dinosaur exhibit knew so much more than I did about fossils. _____

3. The museum fire alarms had both flashing lights and an <u>able to be heard</u> signal. _____

4. The <u>people who came to hear the scientist speak</u> applauded at the end. _____

5. Dinosaurs must have been <u>amazing</u> to see. _____

6. Ping left his <u>eyeglasses</u> in the pocket of his coat, so he couldn't read where the bones of the ichthyosaurus were found. _____

At Home: Together, discuss the meanings of the words *auditorium* and *inspect*.

Meet a Bone-ified Explorer
Grade 4/Unit 6
205

> When added to the beginning of a word, a prefix changes the meaning of the word.
> The prefixes *un-, non-,* and *dis-* mean "not" or "the opposite of."
>
> - *dis* + trust = distrust   to not trust
> - *non* + sense = nonsense   something that doesn't make sense
> - *un* + covered = uncovered   the opposite of covered
>
> The prefix *mis-* means "badly" or "incorrectly."
>
> - *mis* + spell = misspell   to spell incorrectly
>
> Each of these prefixes has a short vowel sound.

Underline the prefix in the following words. Then write the meaning of the word.

1. disobey _____

2. unsure _____

3. misbehave _____

4. nonsense _____

5. unhappy _____

6. dislike _____

7. misunderstand _____

8. disconnect _____

9. unbelievable _____

10. miscalculate _____

© Macmillan/McGraw-Hill

At Home: Together, make up sentences using the words in the exercises above.

Name _____

glider   assured   wingspan   headlines
unstable   applauded   hoisting

Write the word that matches each meaning. Then write your answer in the crossword puzzle.

Across

2. the distance between the tips of a plane's wings _____

4. certain _____

5. a light aircraft that uses air currents to fly _____

6. not steady _____

Down

1. clapped to show appreciation for a performance _____

3. newspaper article titles _____

> An **author's perspective** is his or her point of view. It may include the author's attitudes and opinions about a subject.

Read each passage. Then answer the questions that follow.

Planes are so safe today that no one should be afraid to fly. Flying is one of the safest ways to travel. Far more people are hurt while riding in cars than flying in planes.

1. What is the author's opinion about the safety of flying? _____

_____

2. What information does the author give to support this? _____

_____

Today's airplanes may hold a lot of people, but airlines have taken all the fun out of flying. No one likes to be crowded into a small space for a long time. Airlines make more money when they squeeze more passengers into planes, but passengers get more uncomfortable and less enthused about flying.

3. What is the author's perspective on flying these days?

_____

4. What does the author use as evidence?

_____

5. Write a sentence that the author would agree with about how to make

passengers happier to fly again. _____

_____

© Macmillan/McGraw-Hill

At Home: With the student, write a paragraph that has a clear point of view.

Name _____

As you read *My Brother's Flying Machine,* fill in the Author's
Perspective Map.

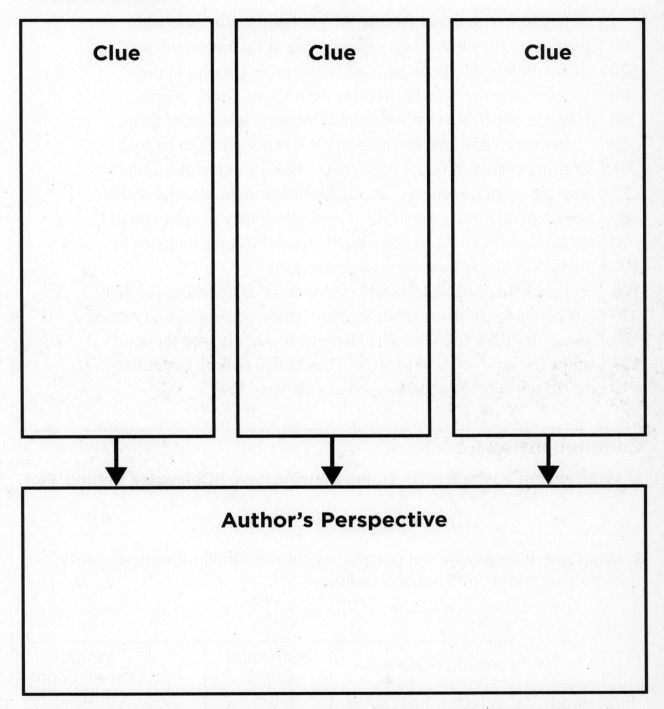

Clue	Clue	Clue

Author's Perspective

How does the information you wrote in the Author's Perspective Map help
you to monitor your comprehension of *My Brothers' Flying Machine*?

At Home: Have the student use the chart to retell the story.

As I read, I will pay attention to my tempo in order to match the action in the story.

	In 1903 Wilbur and Orville Wright built an airplane with
9	an engine. They became the first people to fly a power-driven
20	aircraft safely. Flight became safer and more popular in the
30	decades after the Wright Brothers' first flight. Many people
39	dreamed of becoming pilots. James Banning was one of them.
49	Banning knew that learning to fly was not going to be easy
61	for him because of racial segregation. Blacks and whites usually
71	attended separate schools, ate in separate restaurants, and drank
80	from separate water fountains. There were many people who did
90	not think African Americans should have the opportunity to be
100	pilots. But James Banning was determined.
106	James Banning was born in the territory of Oklahoma in 1899.
116	His parents, like many other formerly enslaved people, had moved
126	there after the Civil War. The Homestead Act allowed them to
137	claim 160 acres of land to farm. They hoped to have better lives
149	far from where they had worked as captives. 157

Comprehension Check

1. What kind of character did James Banning have? **Character, Setting, Plot**

2. What was the opinion that people held about African American pilots during segregation? **Fact and Opinion**

	Words Read	–	Number of Errors	=	Words Correct Score
First Read		–		=	
Second Read		–		=	

© Macmillan/McGraw-Hill

At Home: Help the student read the passage, paying attention to the goal at the top of the page.

Repetition is using a word or phrase several times throughout a poem for emphasis.

Personification is a literary device in which animals or things are given human characteristics.

Read the poem. Then answer the questions that follow.

Operation Migration

A new millennium approaches, filled with hope and cheer.
But will it see the whooping crane for many of its years?
A forgotten resolution to migrate and survive
Keeps the birds from knowing the route or how or why.

A pilot has a brainstorm, filled with hope and cheer.
But will it teach the whooping crane to live for many years?
A pilot and a glider would lead the way and show
The whooping cranes that followed where the route is, so they'd know.

The pilot glances back and he's filled with hope and cheer.
Two rows of flapping whooping cranes follow in the rear.
Suspended in the balance between the Earth and sky,
Will the birds remember? Will the birds survive?

Another nest of hatchlings, filled with hope and cheer.
Another brood of whooping cranes to follow late this year.
A pilot in a glider between the Earth and sky.
Each year more birds remember and the whooping crane survives.

1. Which phrases in the poem are examples of repetition?

_____

_____

2. What is one example of personification in the poem?

_____

_____

© Macmillan/McGraw-Hill

At Home: Point out an object in your home. Ask the student to describe it as if it were a person.

My Brothers' Flying Machine
Grade 4/Unit 6   211

> When added to most present-tense verbs, the ending **-ed** makes them past tense.
>
>   jump + **ed** = jumped   turn + **ed** = turned
>
> Use past-tense verbs to speak or write about events that have already happened.

Answer the questions using the past-tense form of each underlined verb.

1. Did Orv and Will <u>leap</u> up to catch the flying machine?

_____

2. Did the boys <u>fix</u> their toy when it broke?

_____

3. Did the printer <u>climb</u> over the baby-buggy press?

_____

4. What did Will and Orv <u>repair</u> in their bicycle shop?

_____

5. Did Will and Orv <u>learn</u> about lift and drag?

_____

6. Did people <u>appear</u> to witness the first flight?

_____

At Home: With the student, take turns making up new sentences using each past-tense verb.

Name _____

> **Suffixes** are word endings that change the meaning of a
> base word.
> The suffixes -y and -ful mean "full of."
>   *dirty* = full of dirt   *joyful* = full of joy
> The suffix -ly means "in a certain way."
>   *nicely* = in a nice way
> The suffix -less means "without."
>   *breathless* = without breath
> The suffix -ness means "the state of being."
>   *sickness* = the state of being sick

**Circle the suffix in each word. Then circle the correct meaning
of the word.**

1. cloudy

   a. full of clouds   **b.** without clouds   **c.** in a clouded way

2. suddenly

   a. full of sudden   **b.** the opposite of sudden   **c.** in a sudden way

3. powerful

   a. without power   **b.** the state of being   **c.** full of power
                                  powered by

4. shoeless

   a. full of shoes   **b.** without shoes   **c.** the state of
                                                             having shoes

5. kindness

   a. the state of   **b.** full of kind   **c.** without any kind
      being kind

6. loudly

   a. without loud   **b.** full of loud   **c.** in a loud way

© Macmillan/McGraw-Hill

At Home: Take turns making up sentences that include
the words above.

My Brothers' Flying Machine **213**
Grade 4/Unit 6

| overcome | territory | investigates | solitary |
| prehistoric | nutrients | communication | astronomer |

Read each sentence and decide whether it is true or false. If it is true, write True. If it is false, write False, and explain why.

1. An ant *investigates* new discoveries of food with its antennae.

_____

2. An *astronomer* is a scientist who studies ants.

_____

3. Ants *overcome* problems by working alone.

_____

4. Ants guard the *territory* in which they live.

_____

5. Ants are not *prehistoric* creatures because they've been around for only about 500 years.

_____

6. Some insects are *solitary*, which means they like living in groups.

_____

7. Like ants, we get our *nutrients* from the foods we eat.

_____

8. Ants use *communication* to tell each other where to find food.

_____

© Macmillan/McGraw-Hill

Name _____

> Writers use **description** to give their readers interesting facts and details about a topic. Often, description includes information that appeals to the readers' five senses.

Read the passage. Then answer the questions that follow.

The Life Cycle of the Ant

Egg

Ants begin life as tiny white or yellowish eggs. The eggs are oval in shape and less than 1/16th of an inch long. They hatch in two to six weeks.

Larva

Larvae look like small white worms. They don't have legs, and they can't move much. They grow for several weeks to several months. Larvae shed their skin over and over as they grow.

Pupa

During this stage, the ants change into their adult bodies. In the end, they look like white ants. Their legs and antennae are snug against their bodies. After this stage, they are full-grown.

1. Give two details from the passage that relate to the readers' sense

   of sight. _____

   _____

2. Why does the author mention the detail that the eggs are 1/16 of an

   inch long? _____

   _____

At Home: Have the student describe his or her favorite food, including details about how it looks, tastes, and smells.

The Life and Times of the Ant
Grade 4/Unit 6

215

Name _____

**As you read *The Life and Times of the Ant,* fill in the
Description Web.**

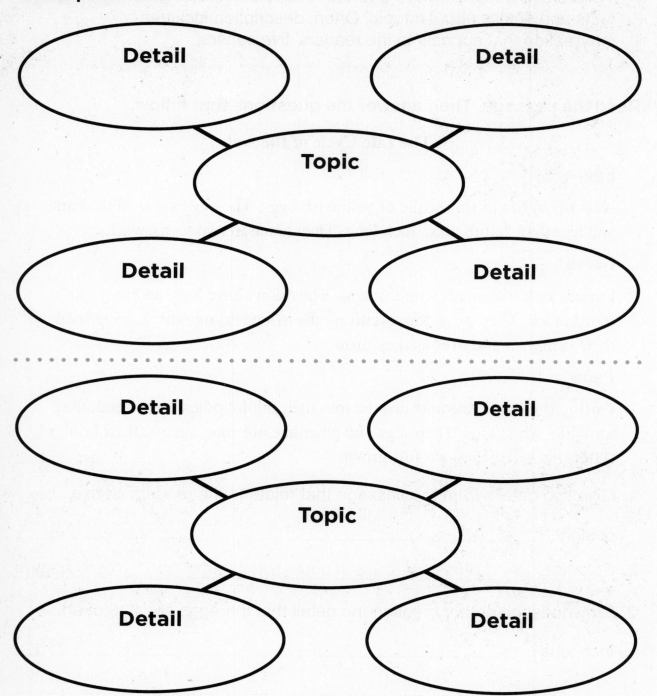

How does completing the Description Web help you analyze the text
structure of *The Life and Times of the Ant*?

At Home: Have the student use the chart to retell the story.

Name _____

As I read, I will pay attention to the pronunciation of vocabulary words.

	Did you know that only the male cricket sings? A
10	male cricket sings to attract a female cricket. This cricket
20	**communication** is made when the male cricket scrapes
28	its front wings together. Each wing has a sharp edge and
39	a bumpy part like a file. First, the cricket lifts its wings.
51	Then, it rubs the sharp edge of one wing against the file
63	of the other. It is almost as if it is playing a violin. Each
77	type of cricket has a different song.
84	Crickets don't have very good eyesight. They depend
92	on their hearing. But their ears aren't on their heads.
102	Crickets have ears on their front legs. Each ear is a small
114	hole with a thin covering.
119	A long time ago, house crickets could be found near
129	warm kitchen stoves. The crickets fed on crumbs that had
139	fallen from the stove. They would also sit near the warm
150	fireplace that heated the home. People often felt comforted
159	by listening to the chirping crickets on cold nights. Today
169	crickets inside homes must find a warm place to hide. 179

Comprehension Check

1. Describe crickets' ears. **Description**

2. Compare how crickets could live in houses in the past and today. **Compare and Contrast**

	Words Read	–	Number of Errors	=	Words Correct Score
First Read		–		=	
Second Read		–		=	

At Home: Help the student read the passage, paying attention to the goal at the top of the page.

The Life and Times of the Ant
Grade 4/Unit 6

217

A **fable** is a short story that teaches a lesson, or **moral.** Fables often have animal characters that behave like people. The **plot** of a fable or other story is what happens in the story.

Read each fable and answer the questions.

A fire ant fell into a river and started to panic. A dove saw this happen, plucked a leaf from a tree, and dropped it near the ant. The ant climbed on the leaf and got safely to shore. "Thank you," said the ant. "I wish I could repay you for your help." The dove waved her wing and flew away. Soon after, a hunter came by and aimed at the dove. The ant ran up to the hunter and stung him on the foot. The hunter missed his target.

1. Why do you think the ant helps the dove?

_____

_____

2. What might the moral of this fable be?

_____

A crow was very thirsty. He found a pitcher and tried to drink from it but couldn't reach the water. Then he started dropping pebbles into the pitcher. With each pebble the water rose higher until, at last, it rose high enough for him to drink.

3. What is the most important event in the story?

_____

_____

4. What do you think the moral of this story is?

_____

© Macmillan/McGraw-Hill

At Home: Read a fable with the student. Discuss the plot and the moral.

Many English words came from other languages. Some words came from Greek, the language of Greece. Knowing the meaning of Greek roots can help you understand other words that use the same root.

Column 1	Column 2
dino- = terrifying	*-logy* = the study of
astro- = star	*-scope* = see
tele- = far	*-saur* = lizard
bio- = life	*-naut* = sailor

Match a Greek root from Column 1 with one from Column 2 to get the English word described. Then use the word in a sentence.

1. star sailor _____

_____

2. see far _____

_____

3. terrifying lizard _____

_____

4. the study of life _____

_____

At Home: With the student, try to identify other words that have the Greek roots on this page.

The Life and Times of the Ant
Grade 4/Unit 6
219

Three different letter pairs can stand for the /ûr/ sound.
    er as in *alert*   *ir* as in *thirsty*   *ur* as in *furnace*
Notice that /ûr/ does not occur in unstressed syllables. When *er*
appears in an unstressed syllable (as in *mother*), the sound is
represented with /ər/.

whirling	fertilizer	dirty	nurture
scurry	returns	perfect	surface

**Complete each sentence with a word from the list. Circle the
stressed syllable in each word.**

1. Ants come to the _____ to look for food.

2. They _____ along the ground, leaving
   scent trails.

3. The leaves and petals they bring back are used as _____.

4. The queen ant flies into a cloud of _____ male ants.

5. The queen ant _____ to dig a hole and begin laying
   her eggs.

6. Nurse ants feed and _____ the larvae.

7. Digging holes is hard, _____ work, but that doesn't seem
   to bother the ants.

8. Their mandibles are _____ for scooping the soil to make
   new tunnels.

At Home: Ask the student to identify the letters that stand
for the /ûr/ sound in each of the words above.

Name _____

A. Draw a line to match each definition to the vocabulary word that has a similar meaning.

Column 1   **Column 2**

1. one who studies the stars and planets   a. overcome

2. sparkled or flashed   b. hoisting

3. lifting a heavy object,
   usually with a machine   c. eavesdropping

4. listening in on someone else's
   conversation without them
   knowing you are there   d. astronomer

5. be victorious over   e. glinted

B. Complete each sentence with a vocabulary word listed in the box.

| headlines | glider | outstretched | logical | wistfully |

6. The baby walked towards my grandmother's _____ arms.

7. Dad and I scanned the _____ to find the article about dinosaurs.

8. I wonder what it's like to fly in a _____.

9. It doesn't seem _____ to carry an umbrella on a sunny day.

10. Jon watched _____ as the ice cream truck drove away.

C. Write the vocabulary word that completes each sentence.

> stumbled upon   inspected   annoyed   wingspan   communication

11. The inventors must have been _____ when their first attempts to fly failed.

12. After having _____ the dinosaur skeleton, the archaeology student became famous.

13. Do you know which airplane has the greatest _____?

14. What means of _____ do ants use to warn the rest?

15. We _____ the nugget closely to determine if it was real gold.

D. Match each vocabulary word to its definition.

Column 1

16. circular

17. unstable

18. reference

19. assured

20. solitary

Column 2

a. living or being alone

b. certain

c. a source of reliable information

d. round

e. not steady